Calm
Dot-to-Dot

Calm

Dot-to-Dot

**More than 150 soothing images
to discover**

ARCTURUS

ARCTURUS

This edition published in 2017 by Arcturus Publishing Limited
26/27 Bickels Yard, 151–153 Bermondsey Street,
London SE1 3HA

ISBN: 978-1-78428-628-6
CH005690NT
Supplier 29, Date 0317, Print run 5988

Printed in China

Created for children 10+

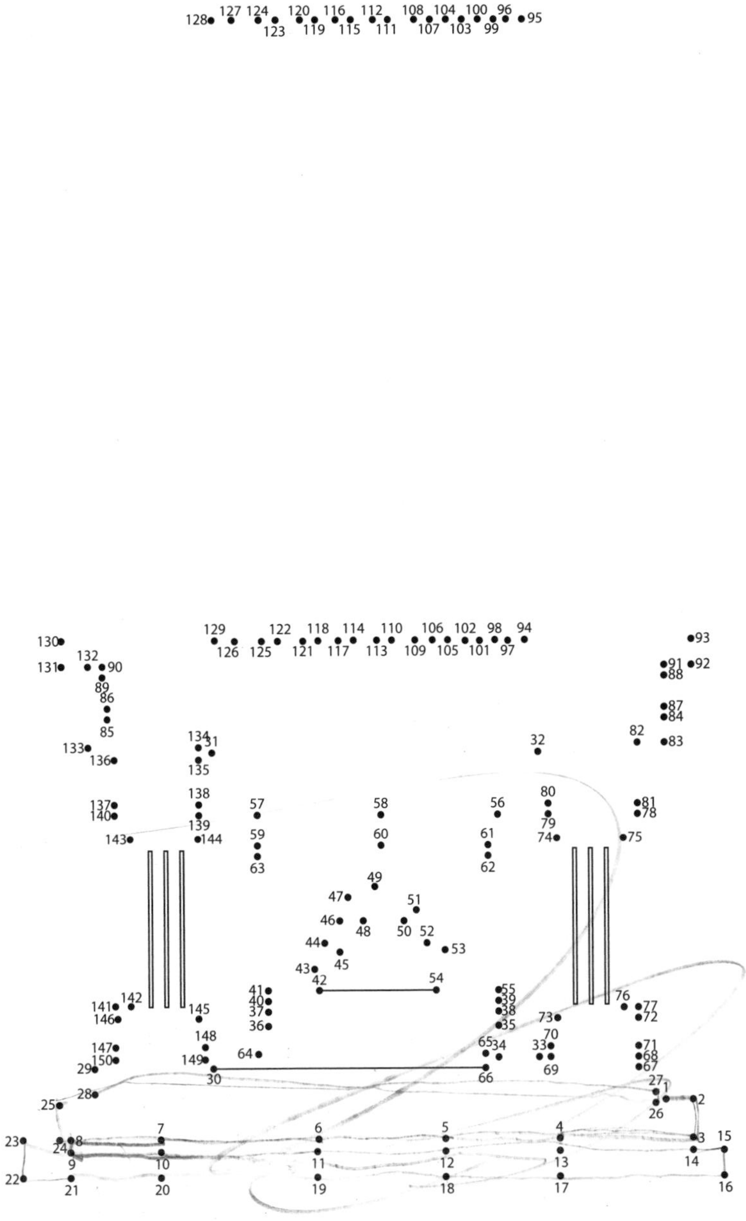

128 127 124 120 116 112 108 104 100 96 95
123 119 115 111 107 103 99

129 122 118 114 110 106 102 98 94
126 125 121 117 113 109 105 101 97

130 93
131 132 90 91 92
89 88
86 87 84
85 82 83
133 134 131
136 135

137 138 57 58 56 80 81
140 139 60 61 79 78
143 144 59 62 74 75
63

47 49
46 48 50 52 53
44 45
43 42 54
41 55
40 39 76
37 38 73 77
36 35 72
141 142 70
146 145 65 34 33
147 148 71
150 149 64 69 68
29 30 66 67
28 27
25 26 2

23 6 5 4 3 15
8 24 7 11 12 13 14
9 10 19 18 17 16
22 21 20

9

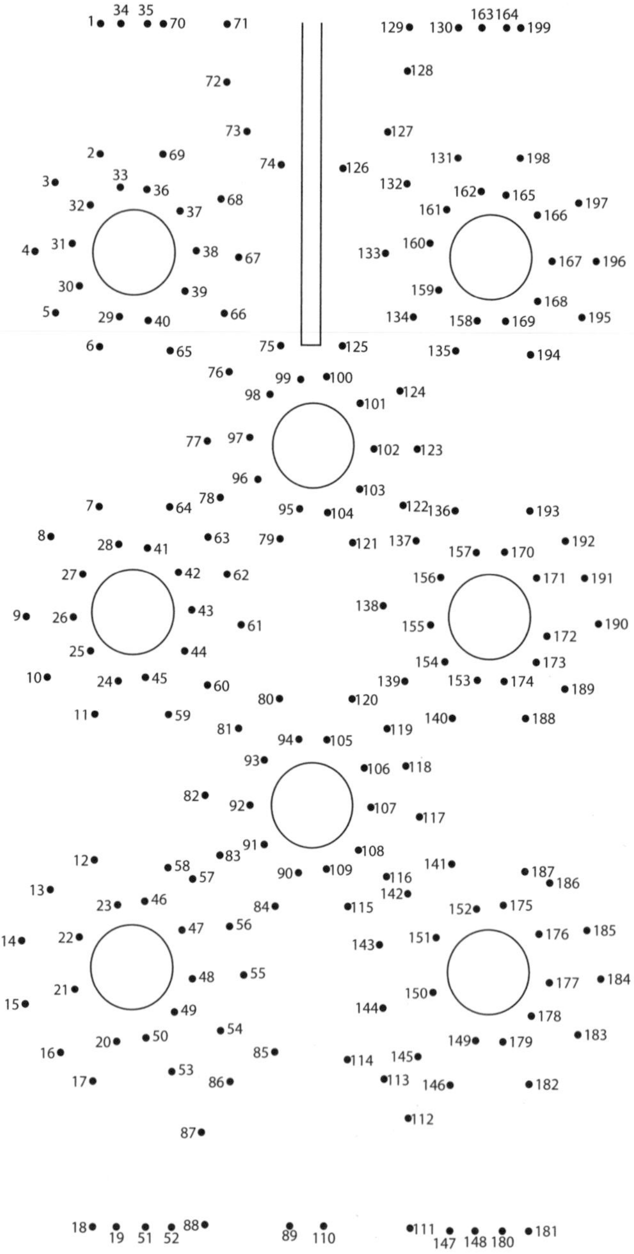

10

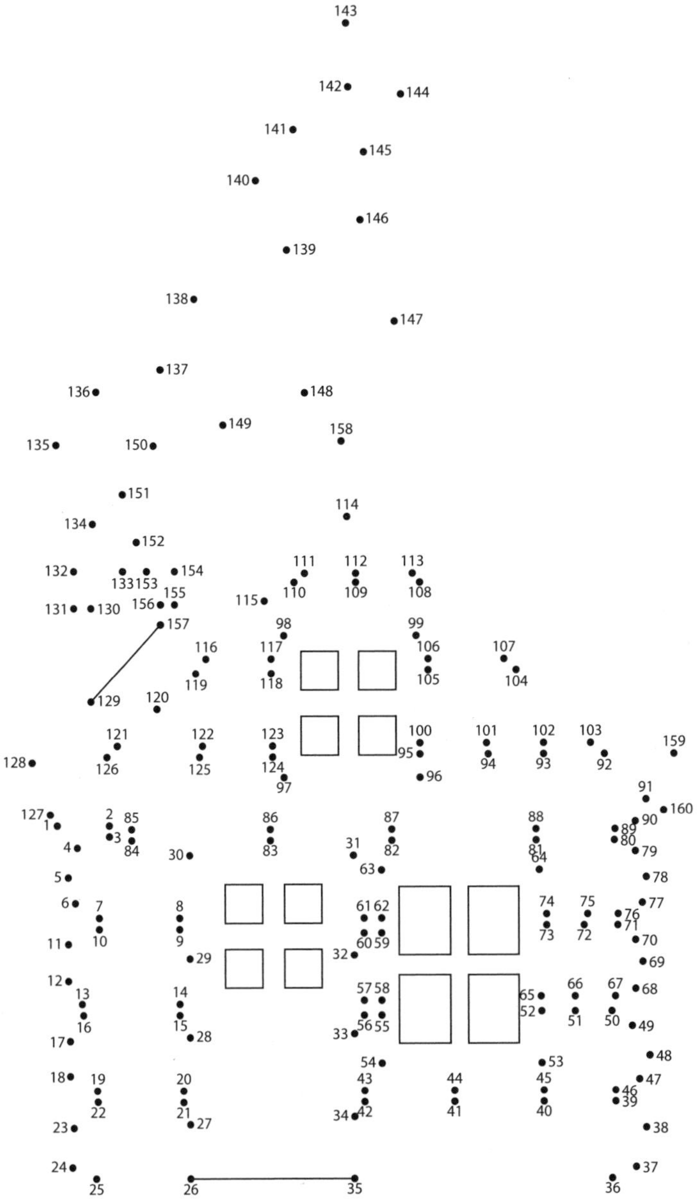

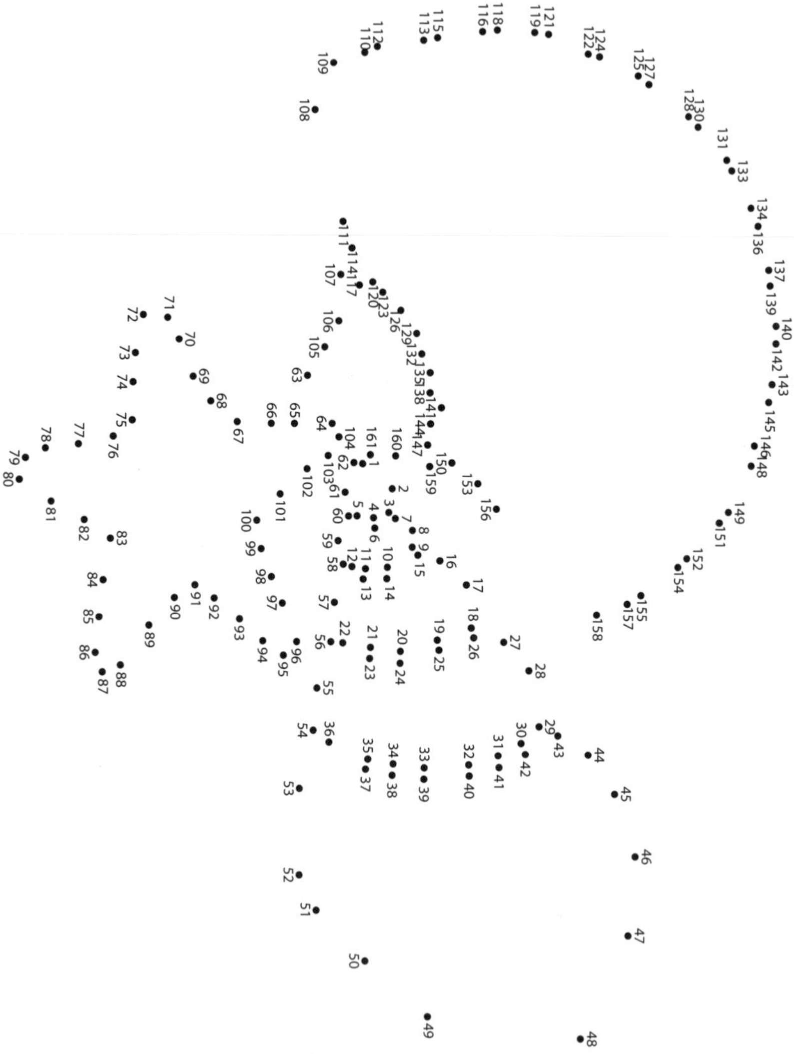

12

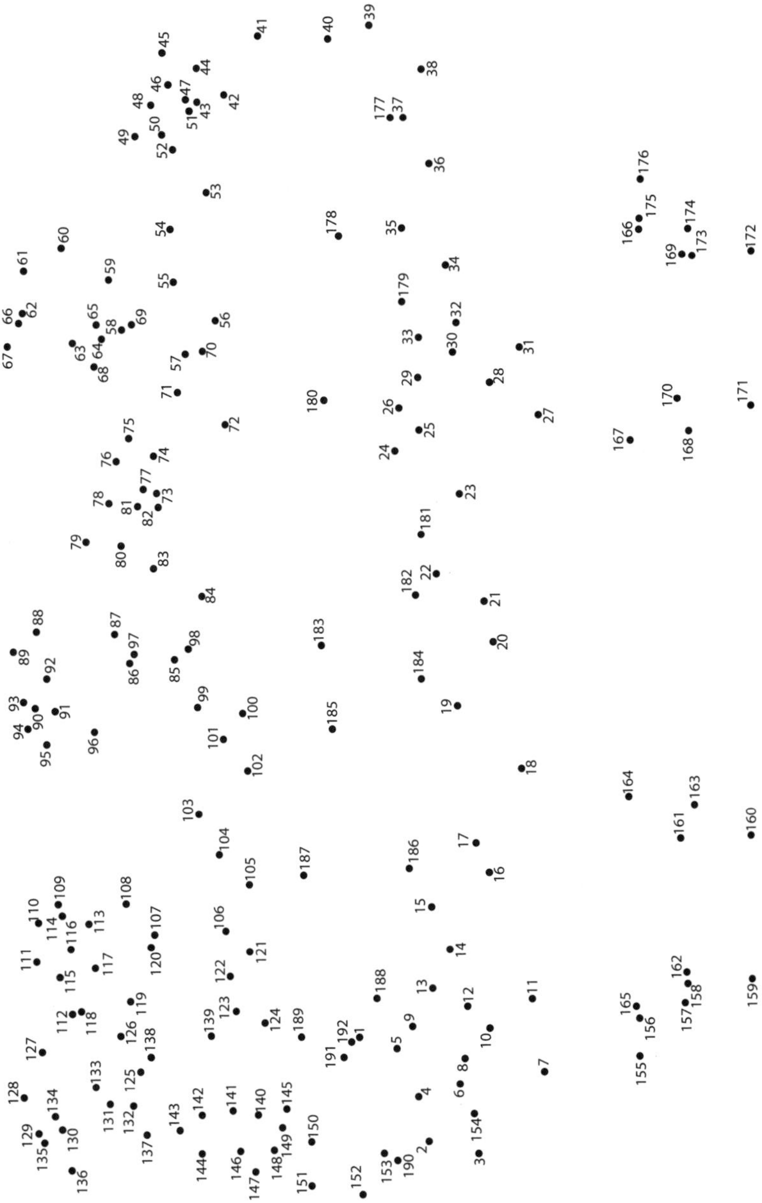

13

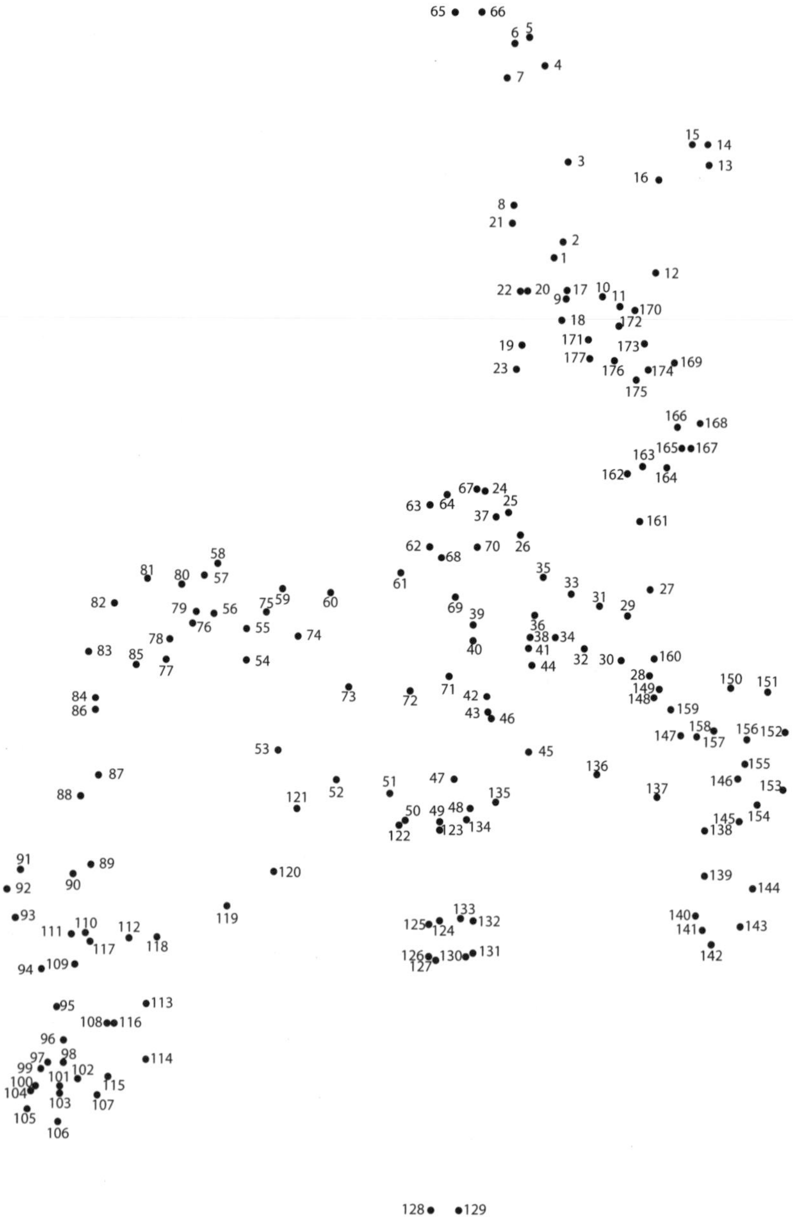

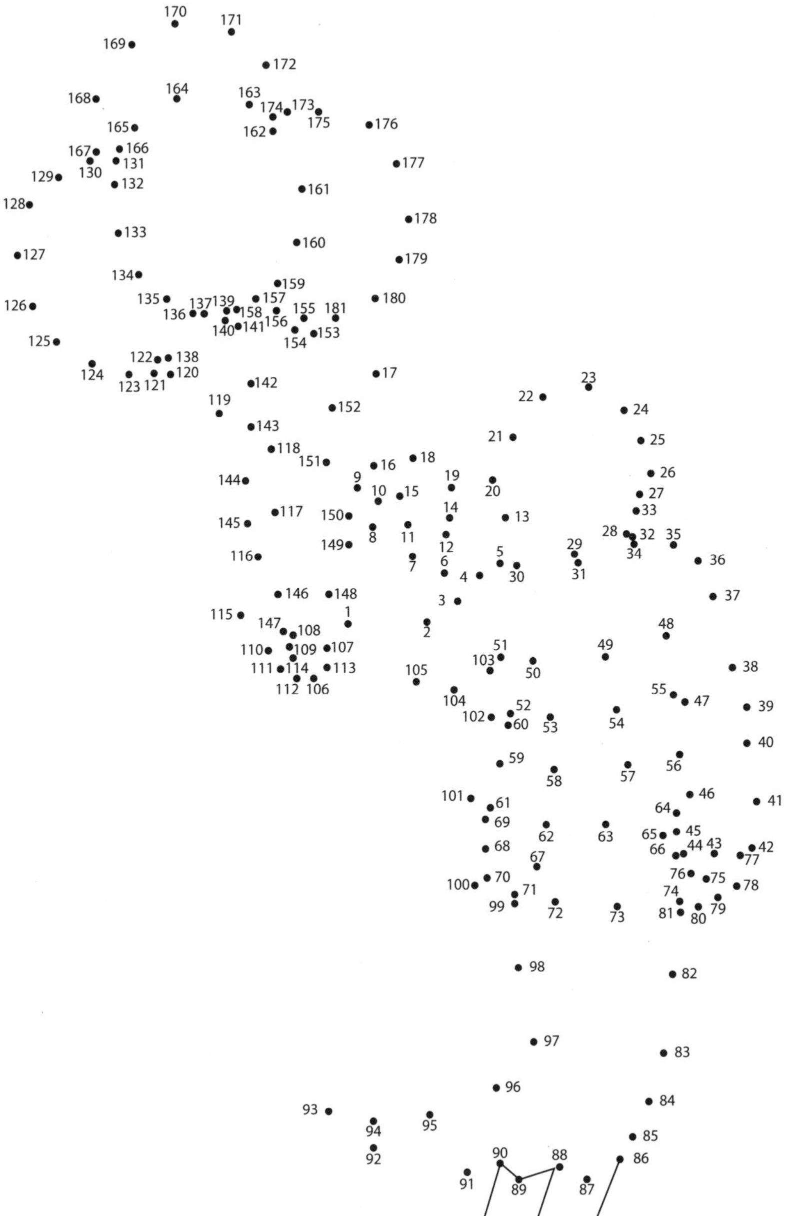

15

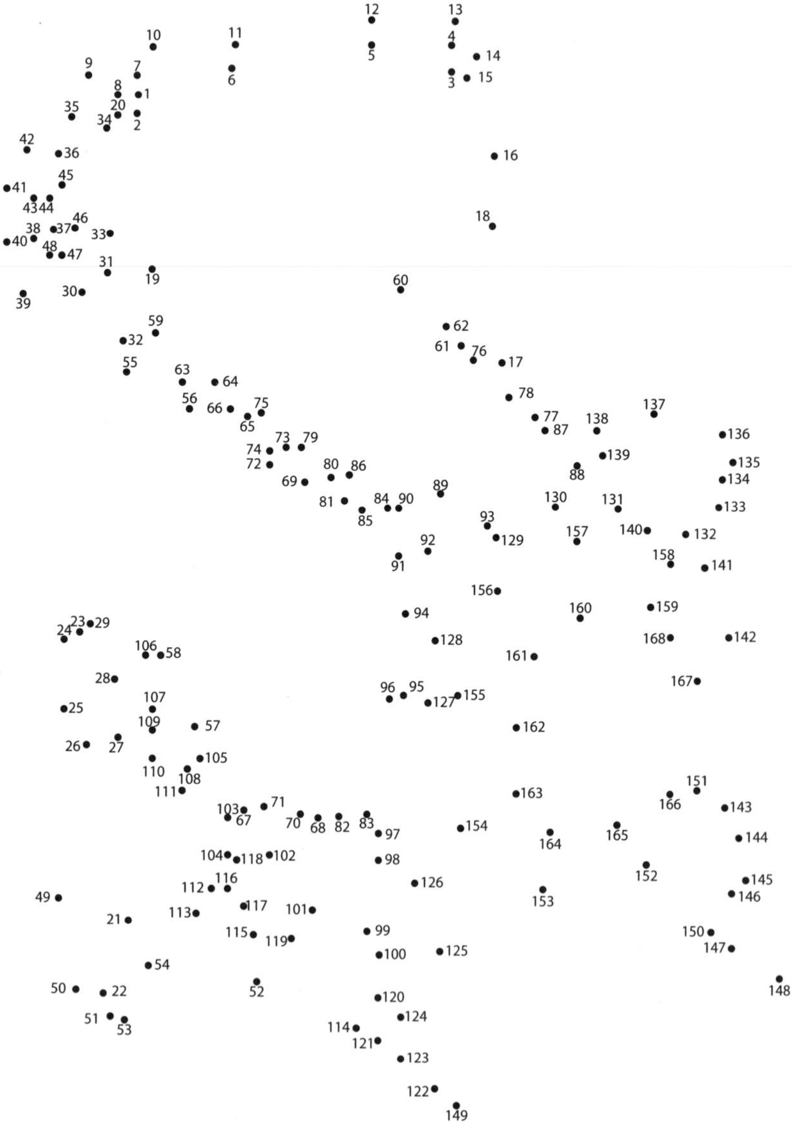

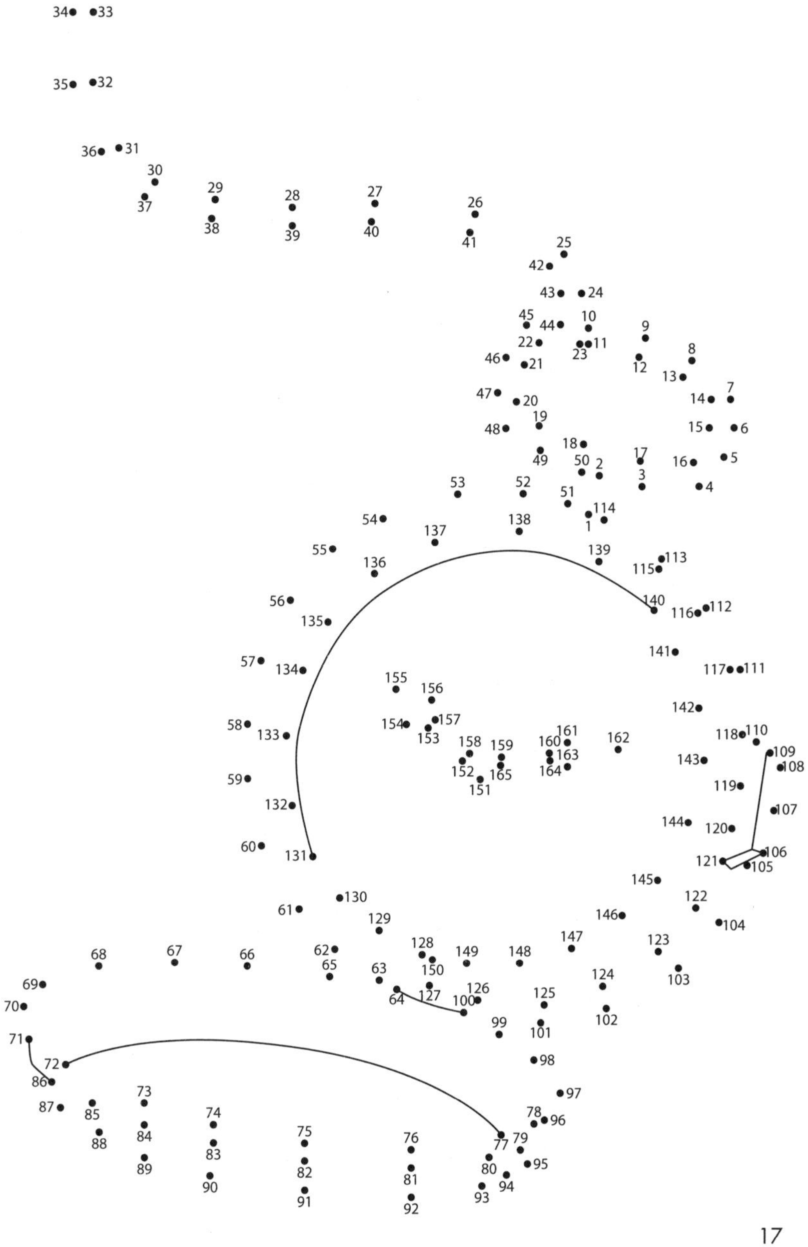

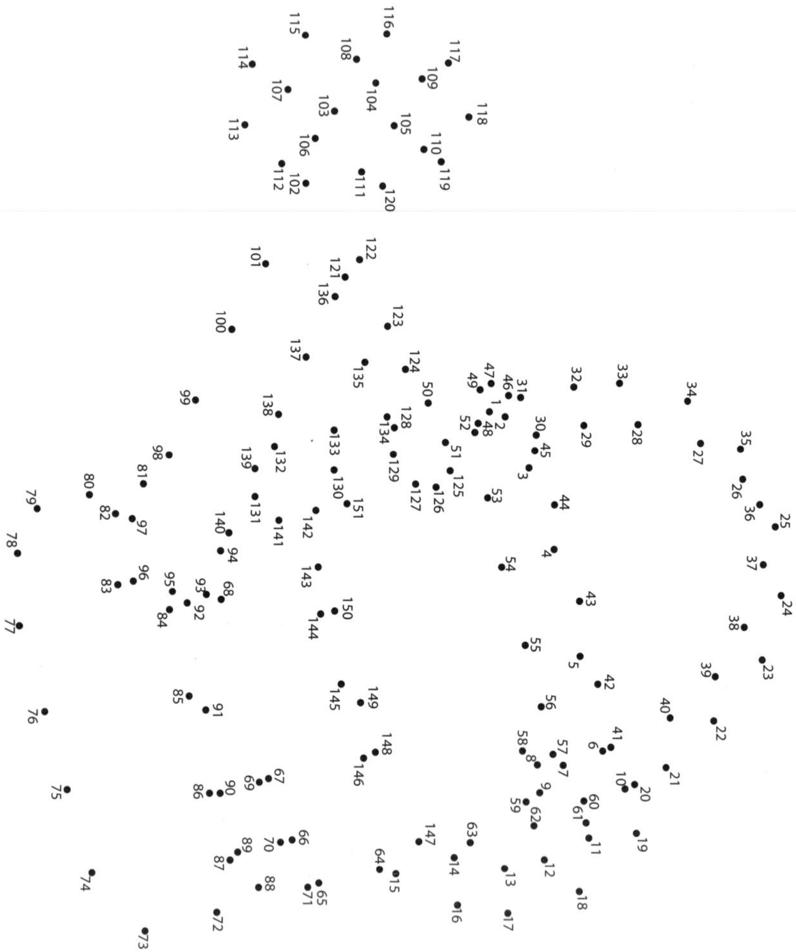

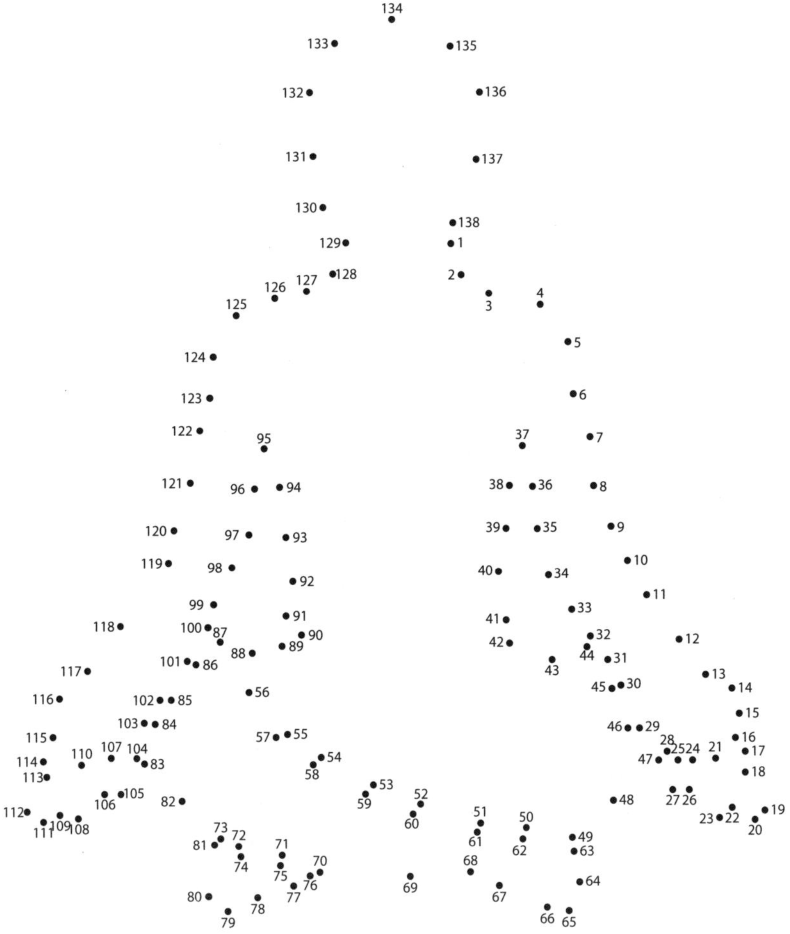

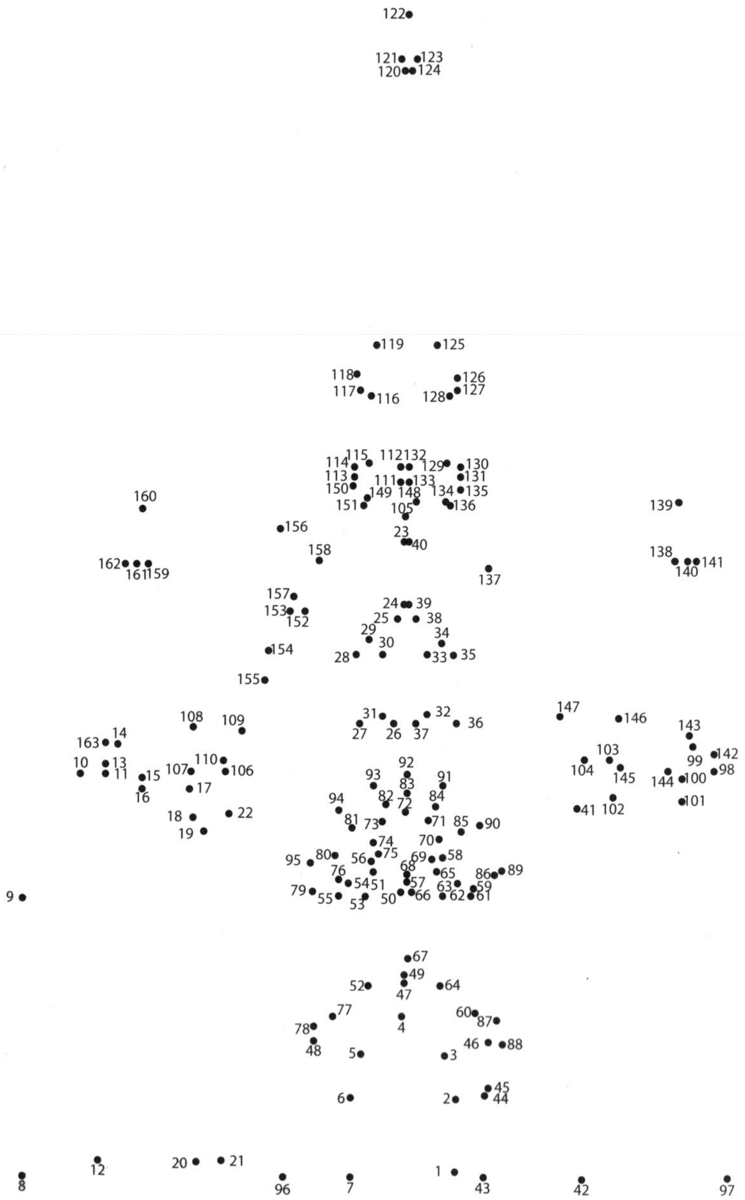

20

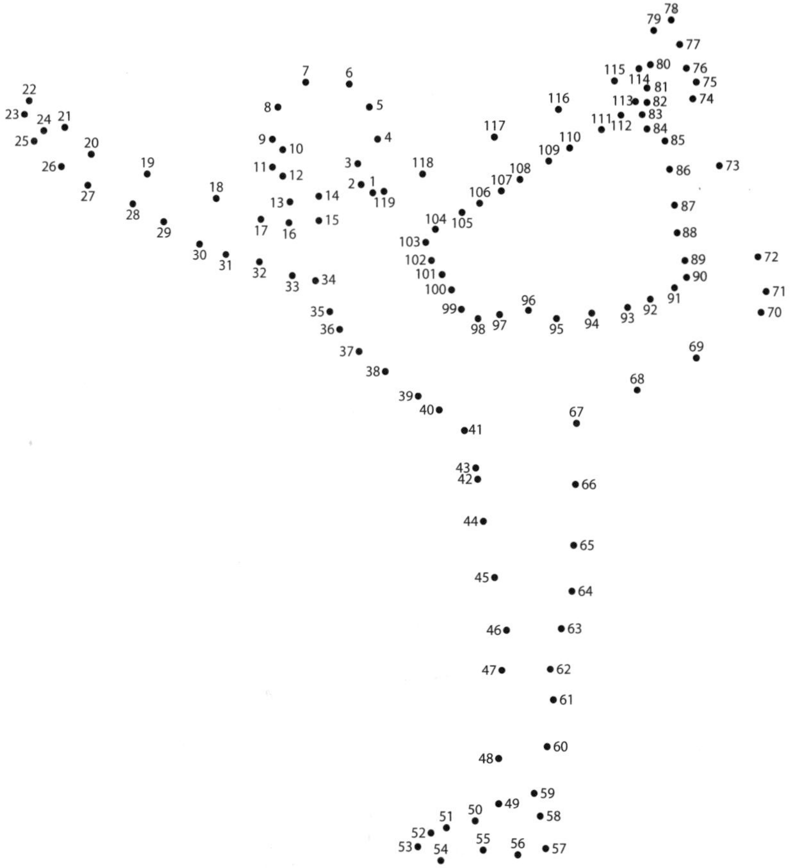

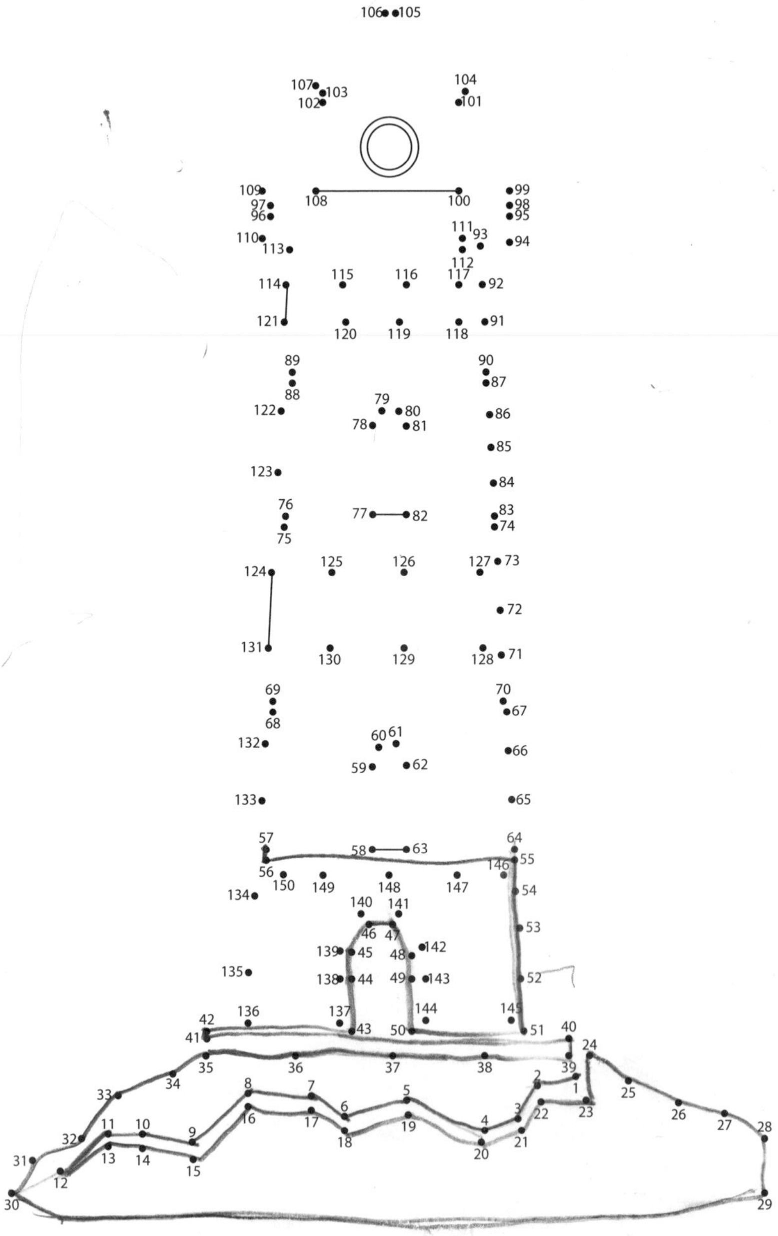

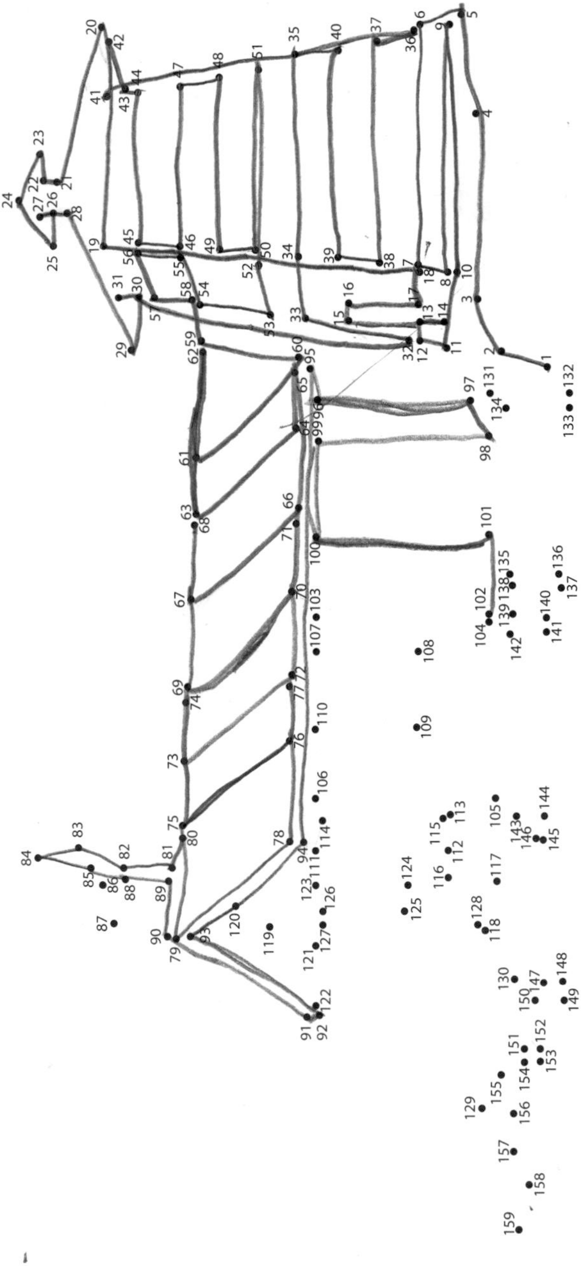

23

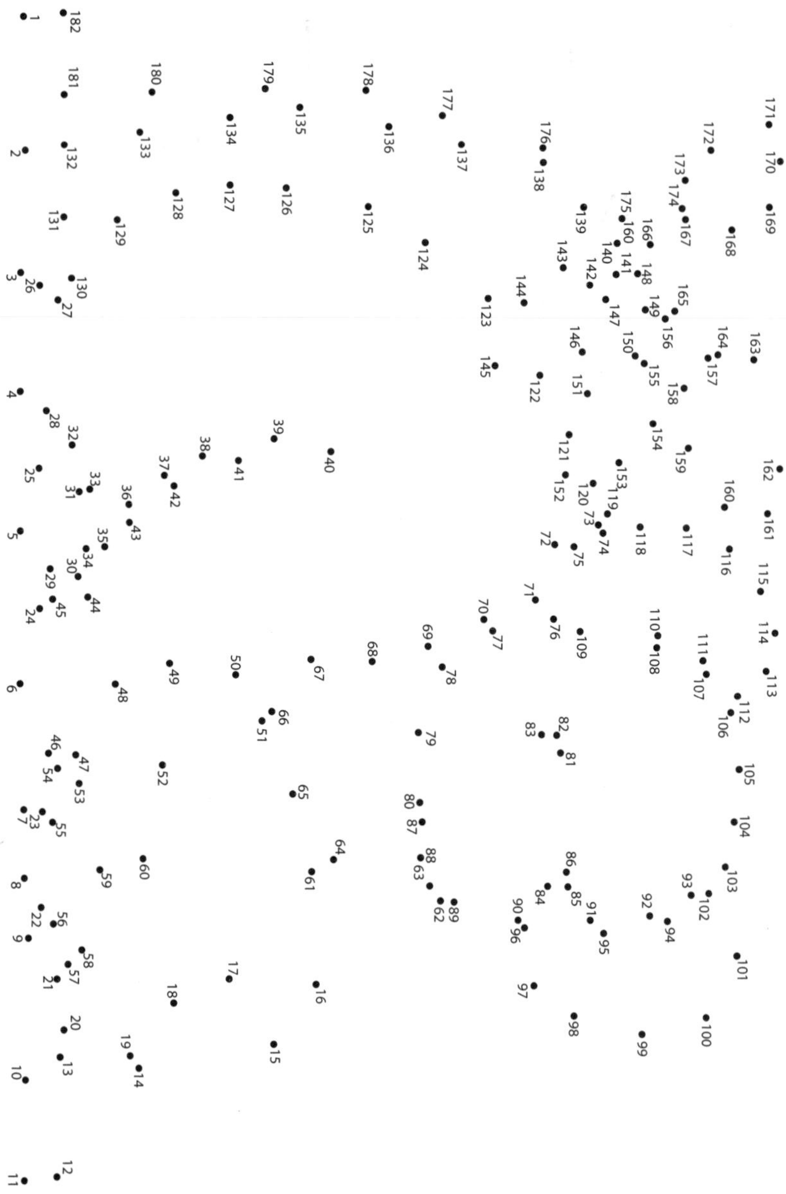

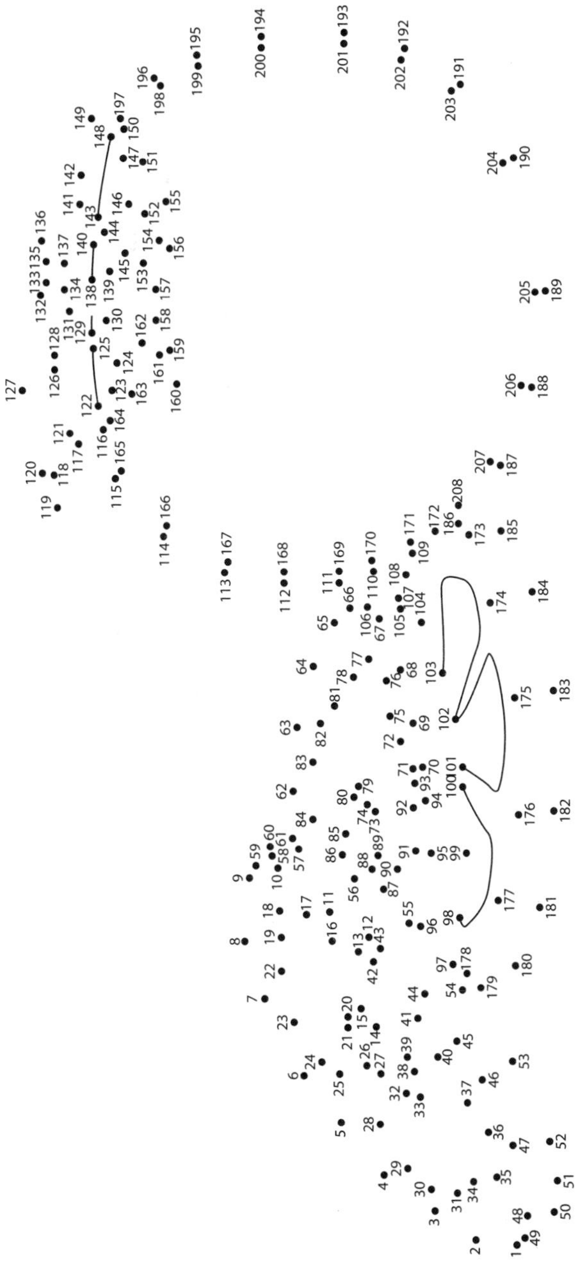

25

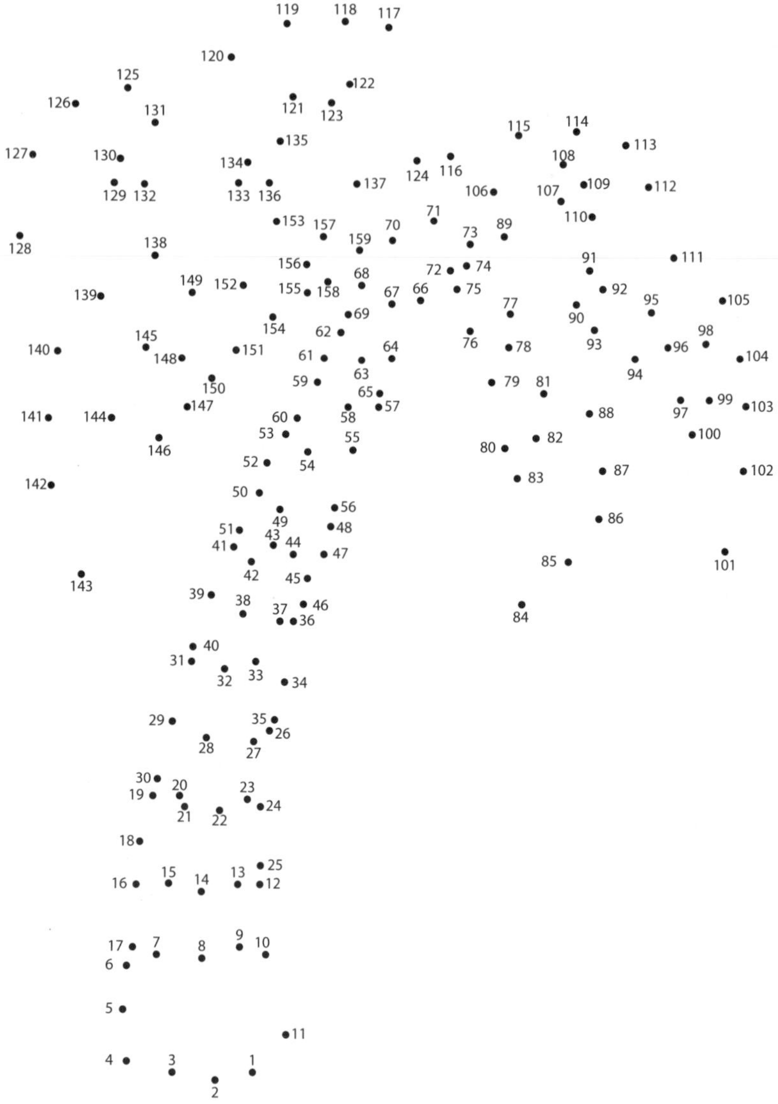

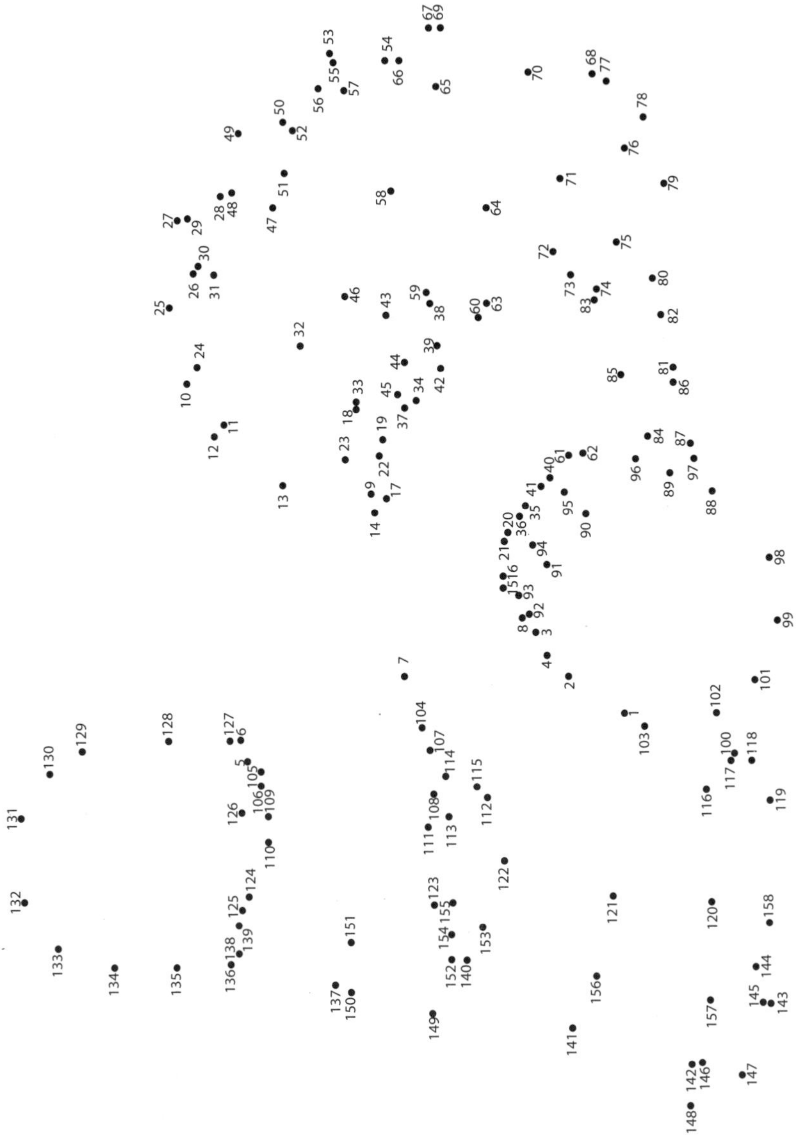

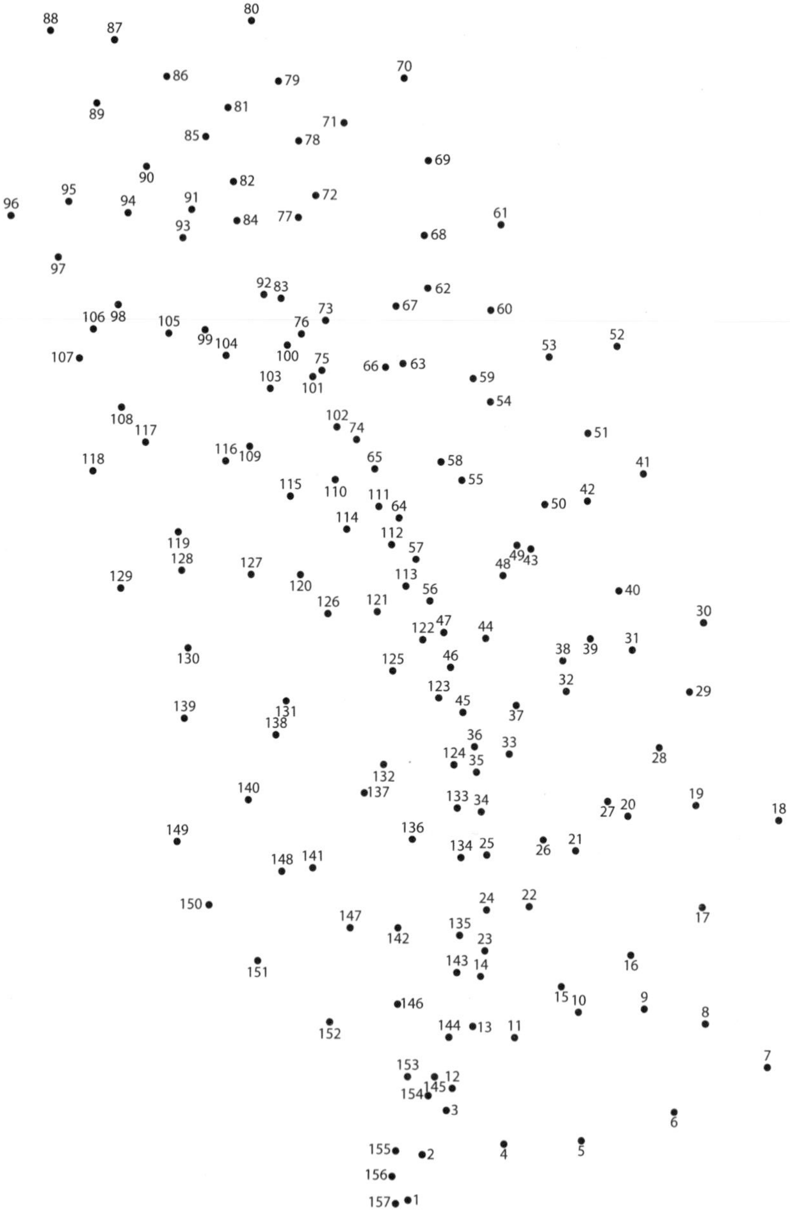

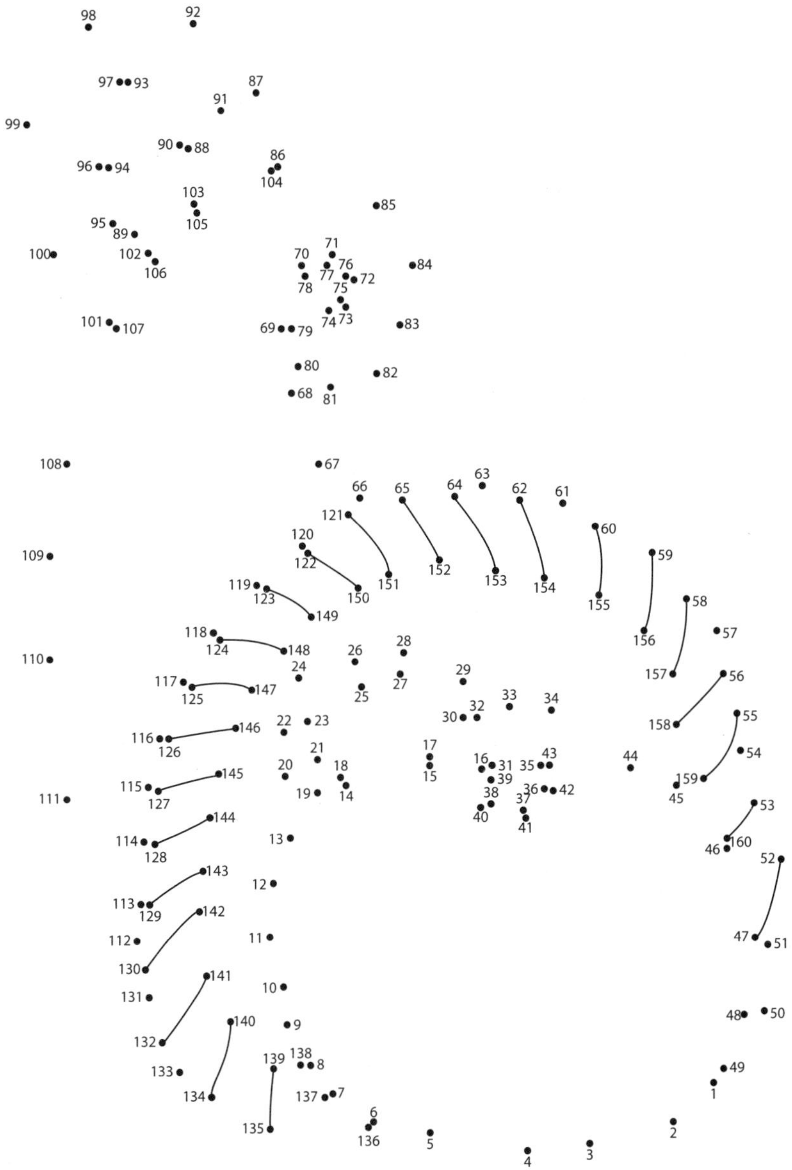

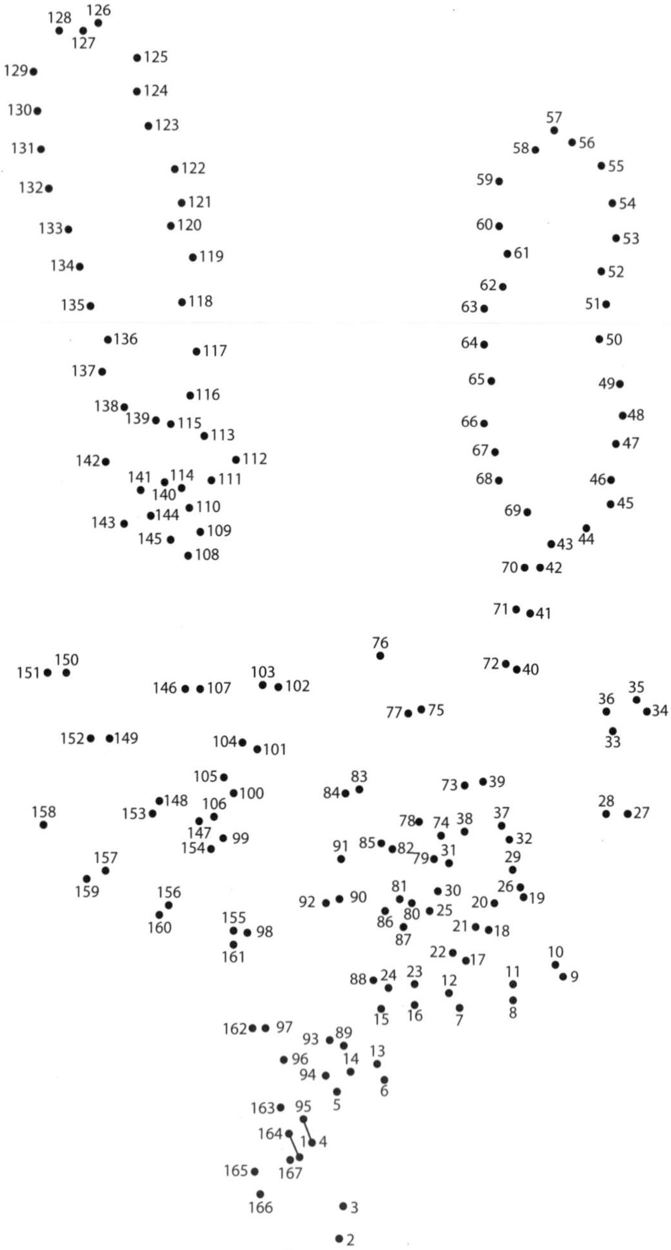

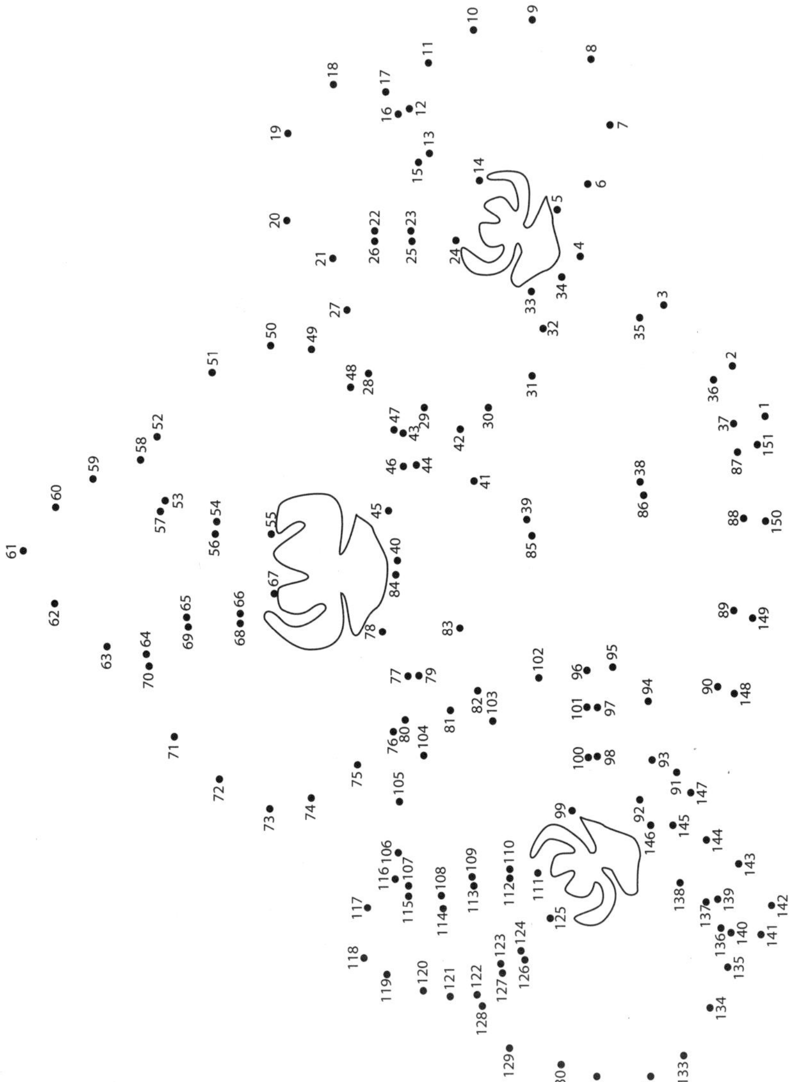

31

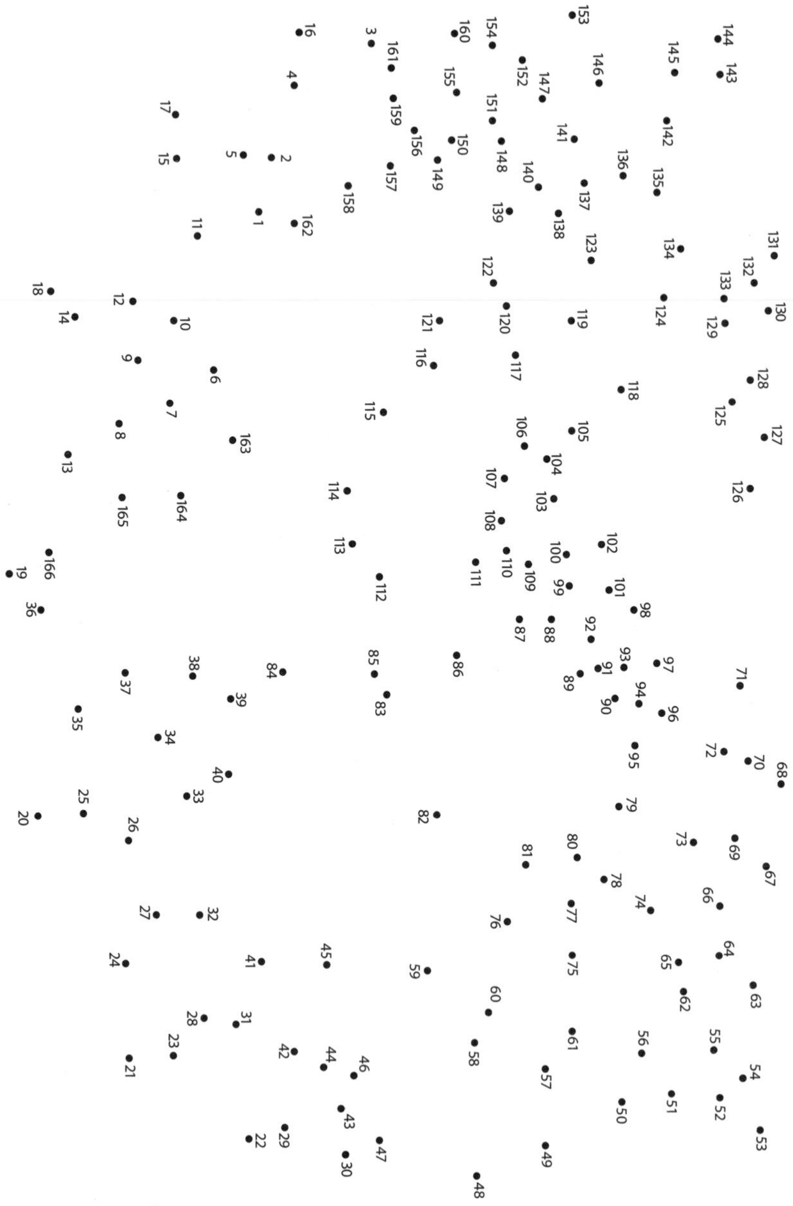

32

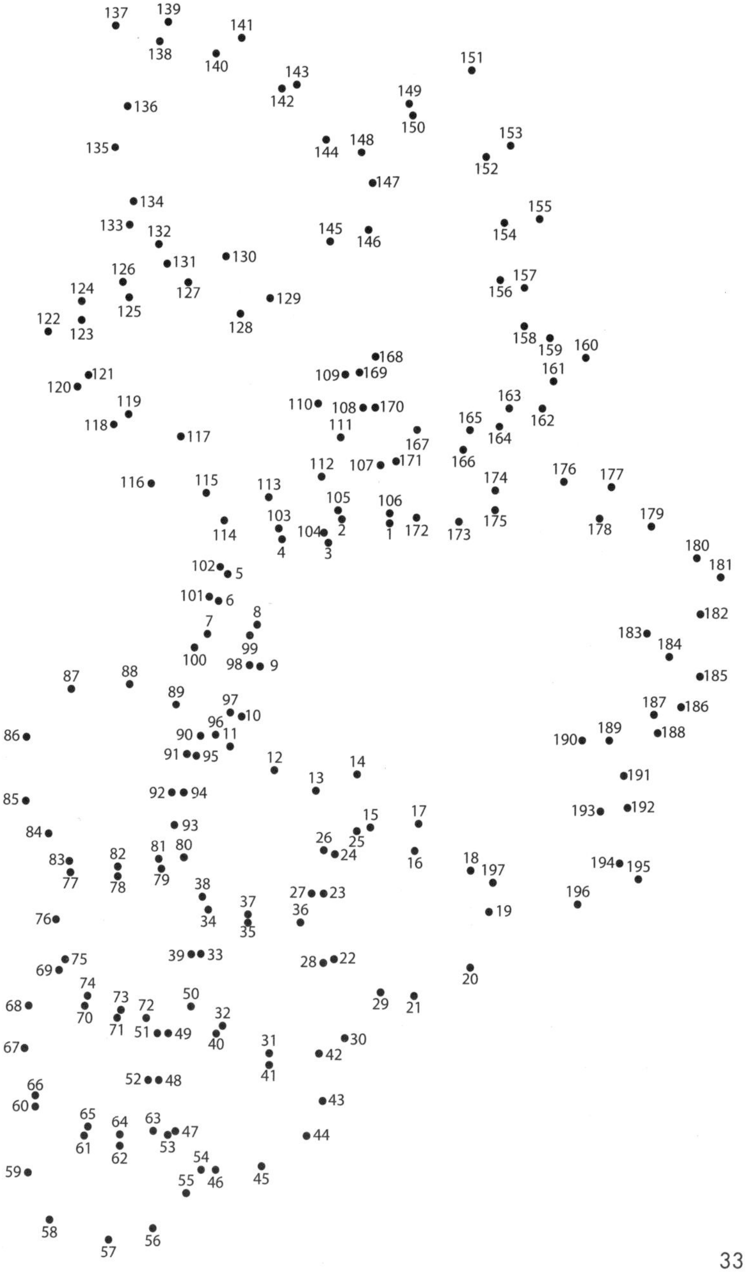

33

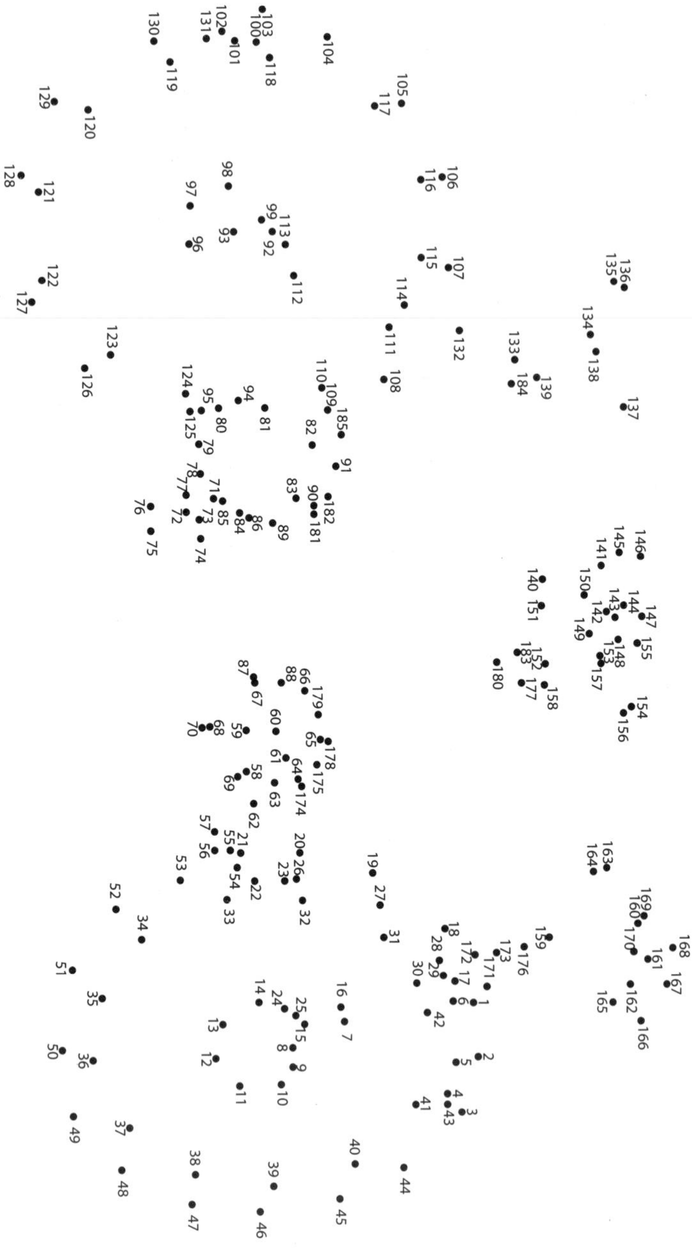

34

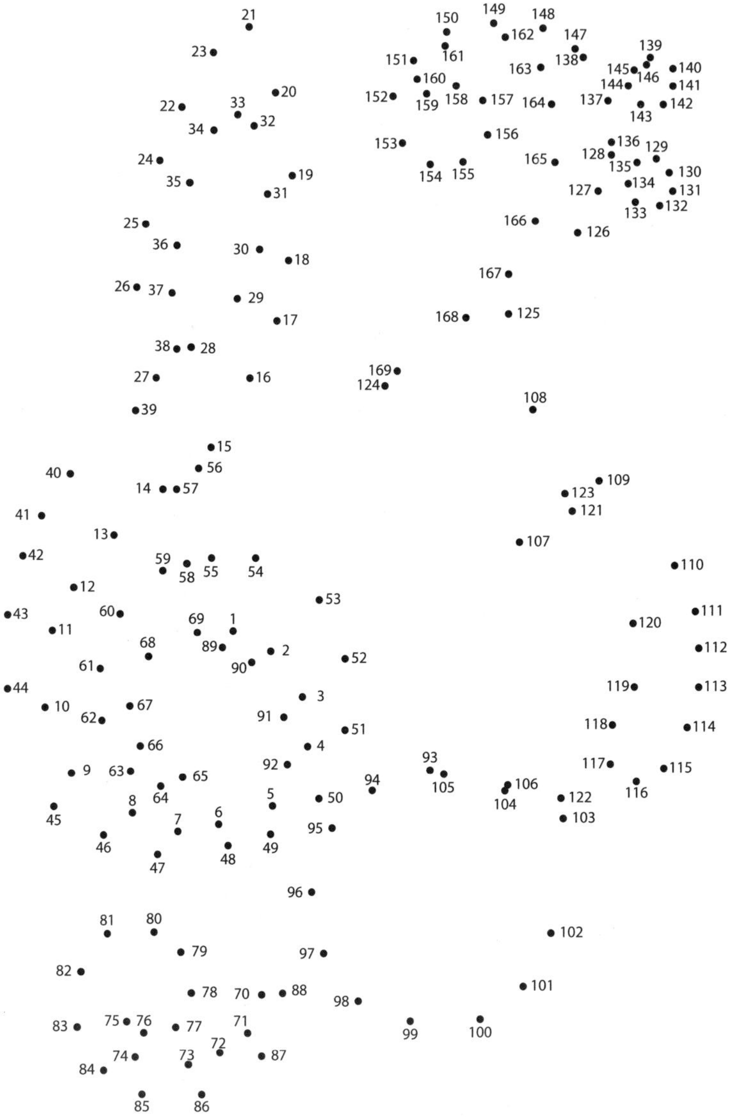

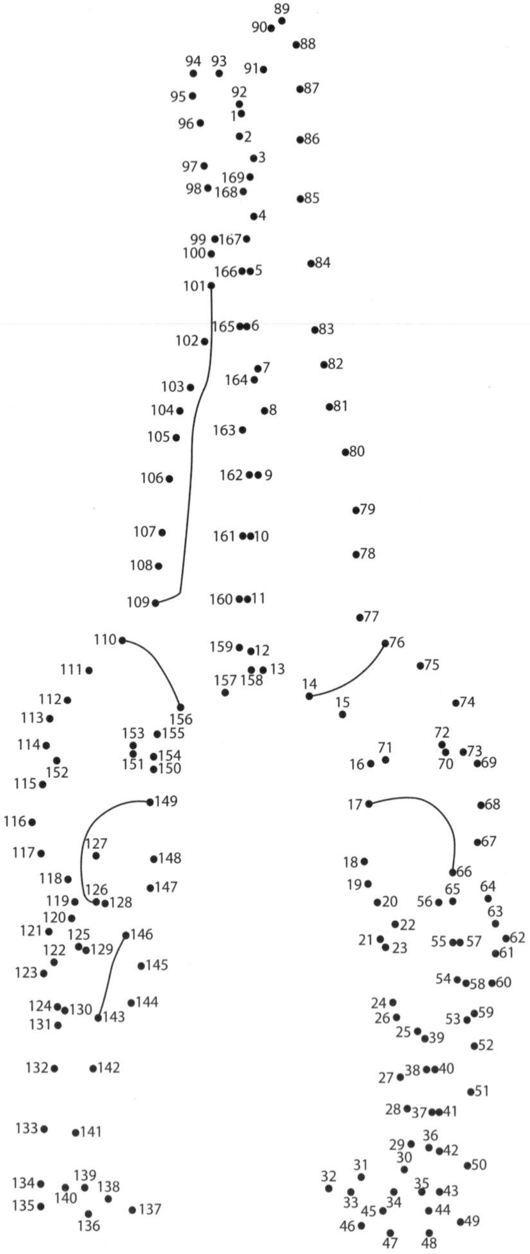

36

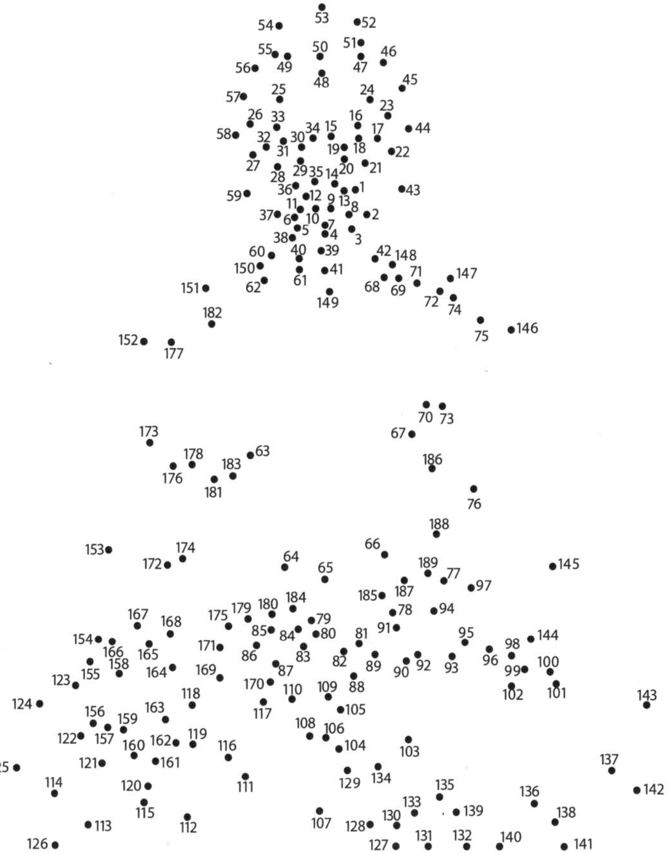

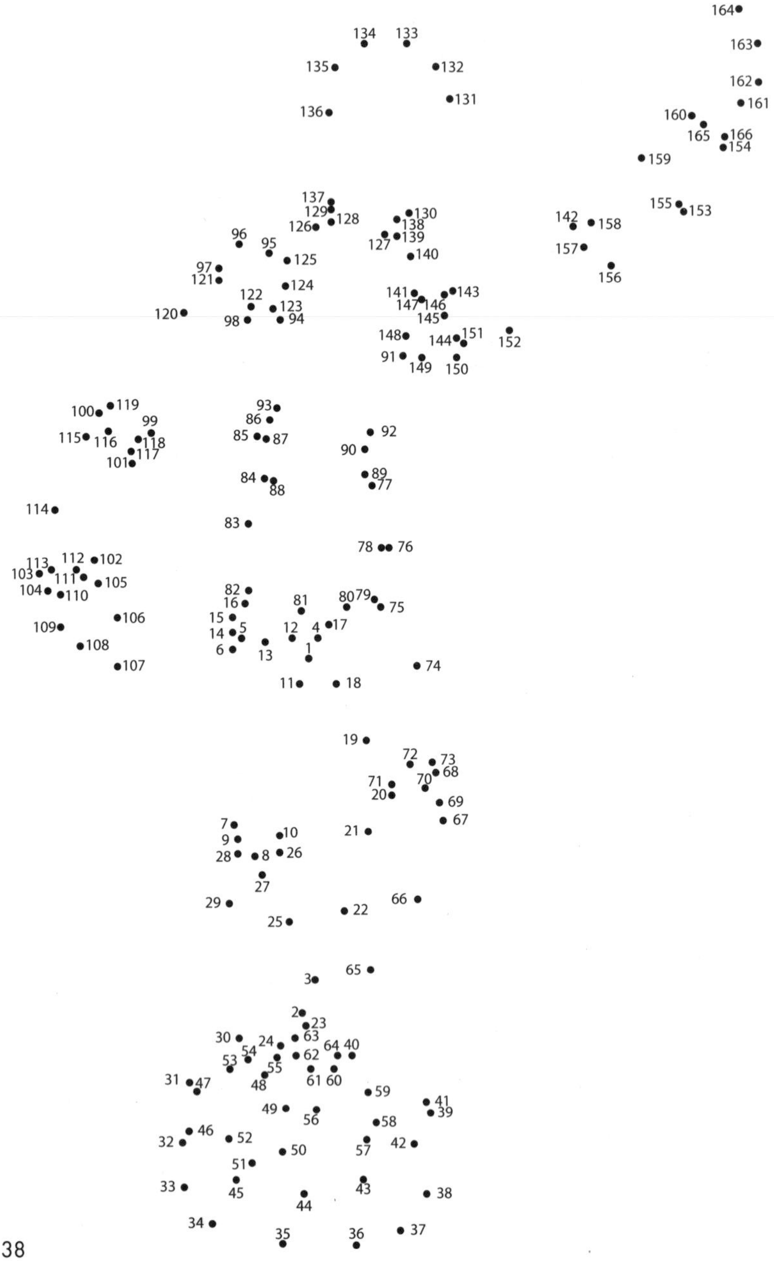

38

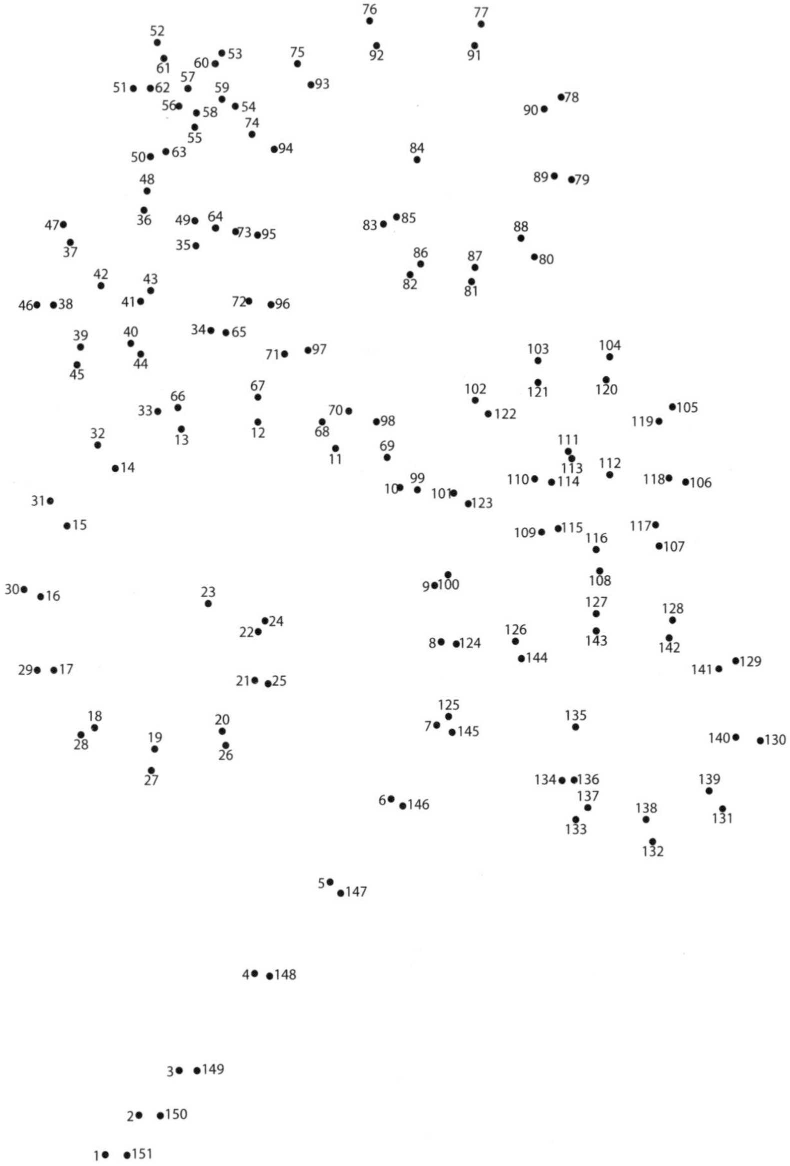

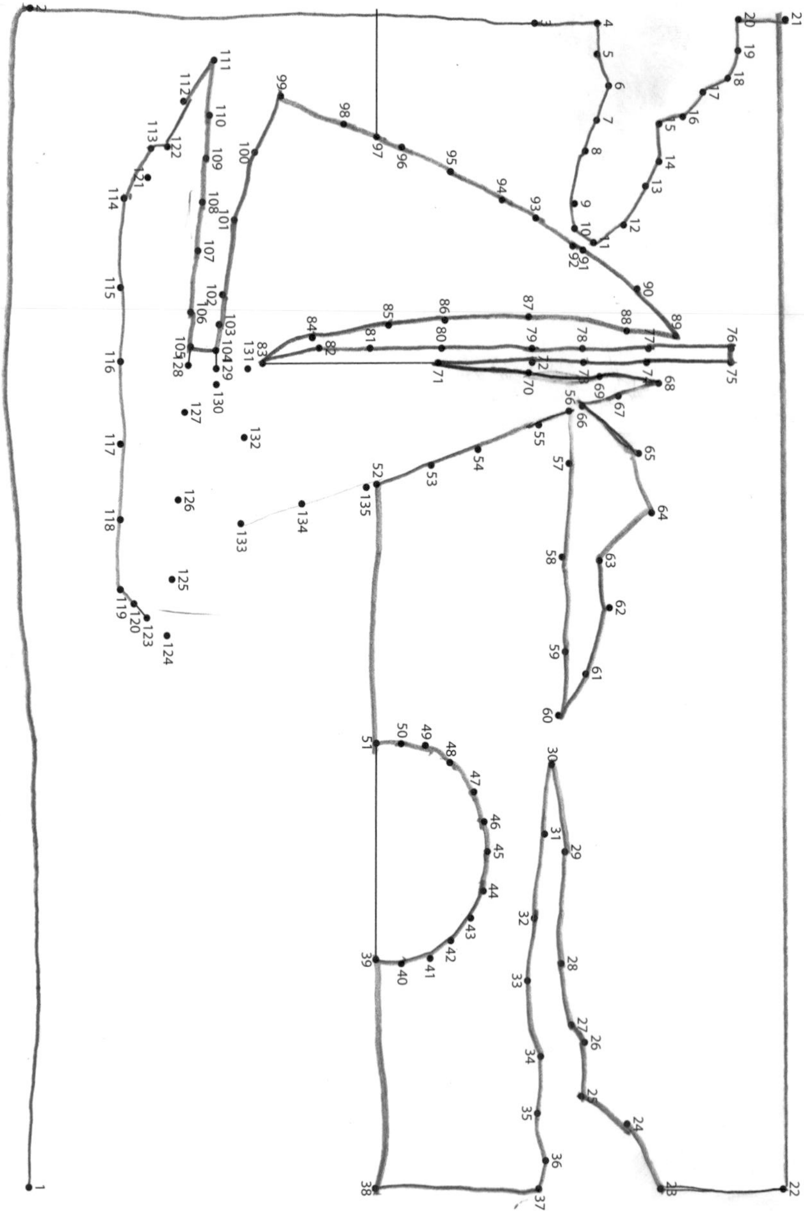

40

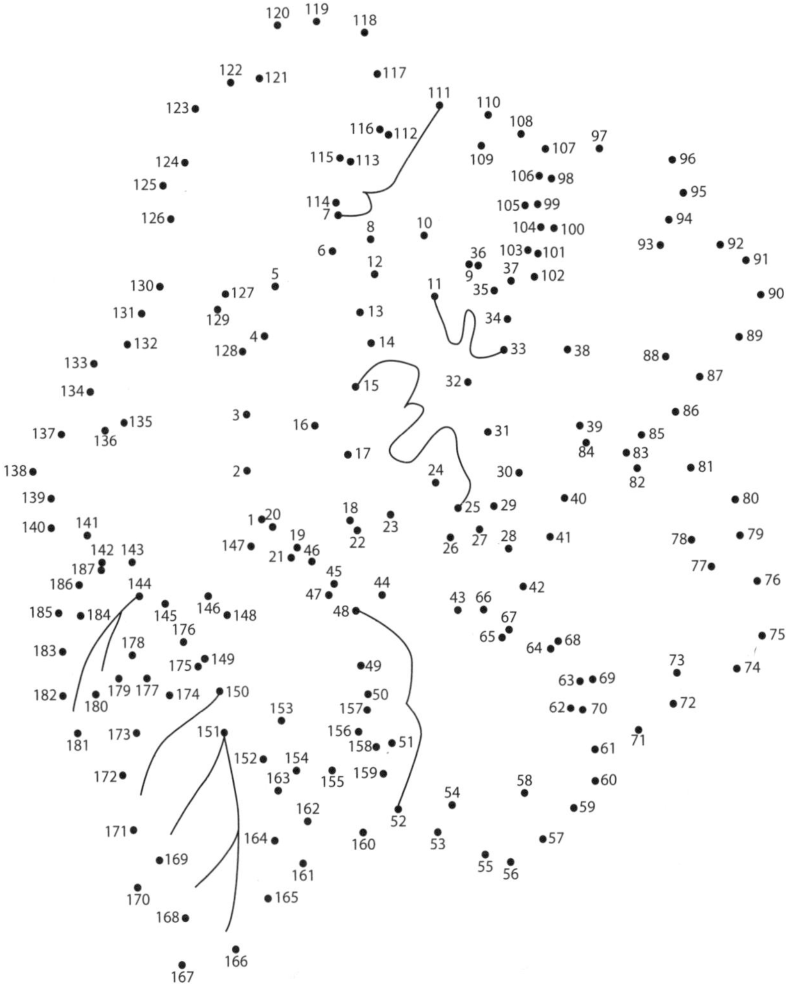

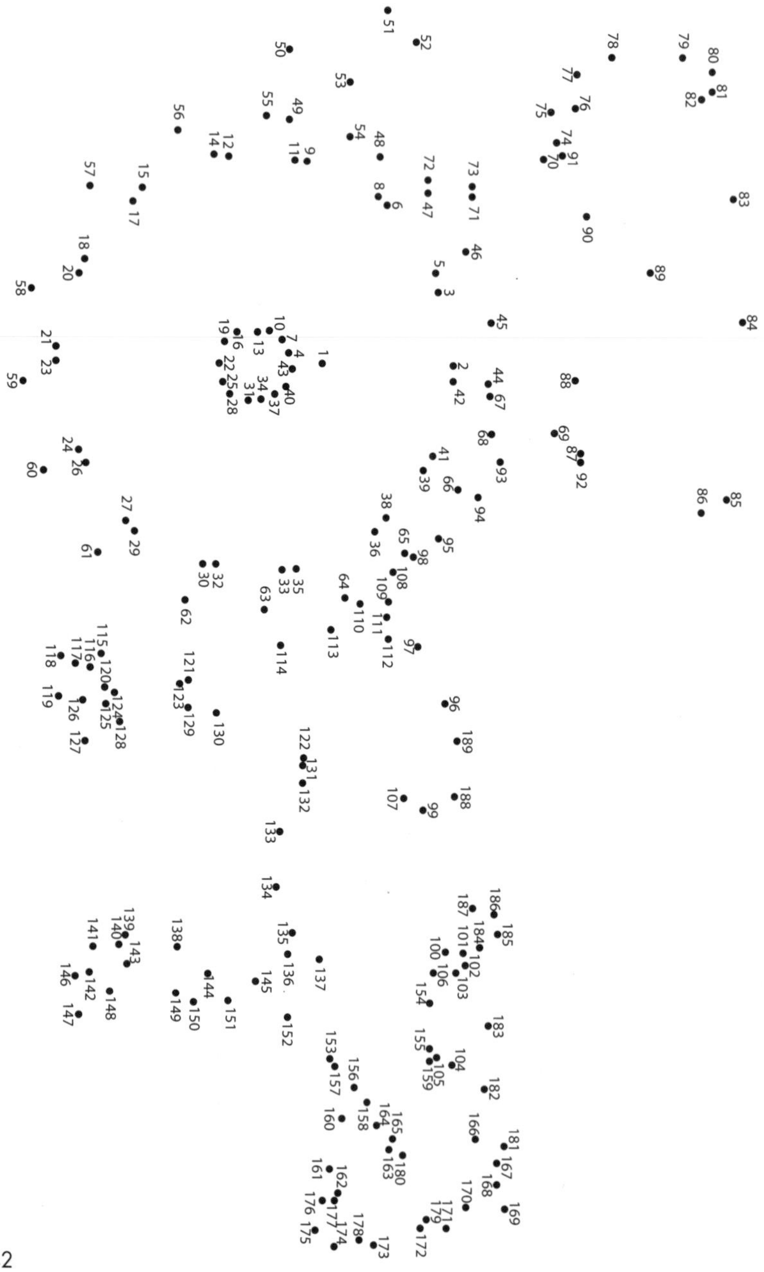

42

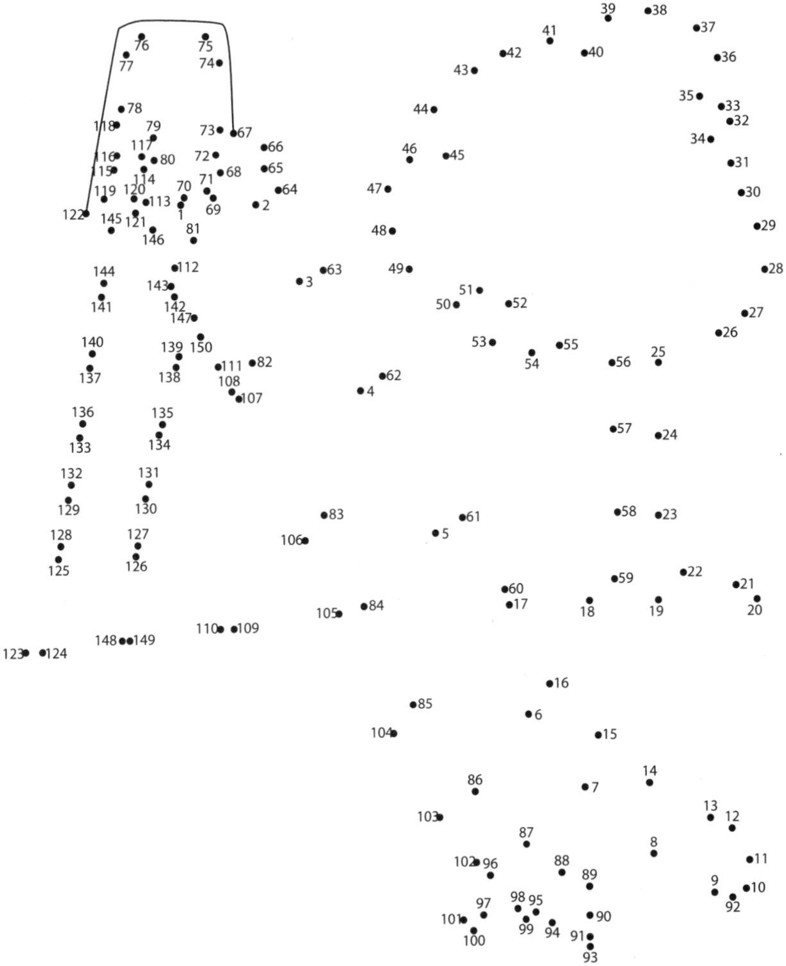

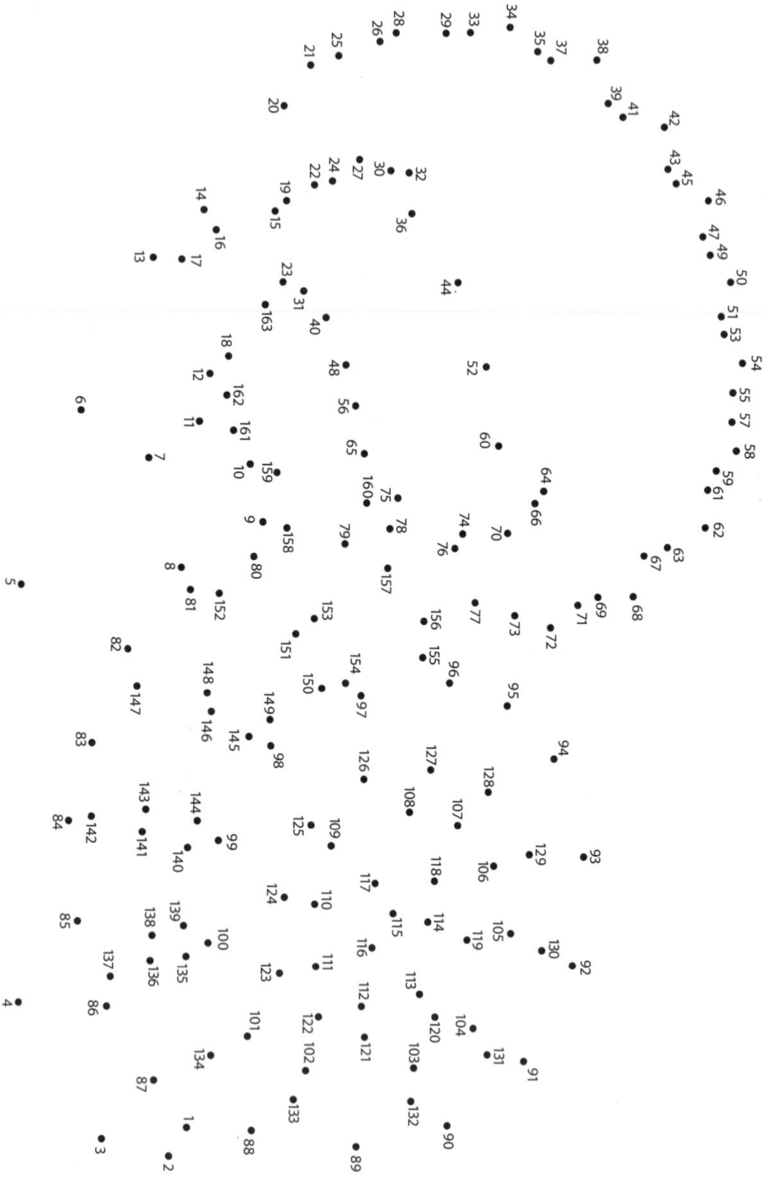

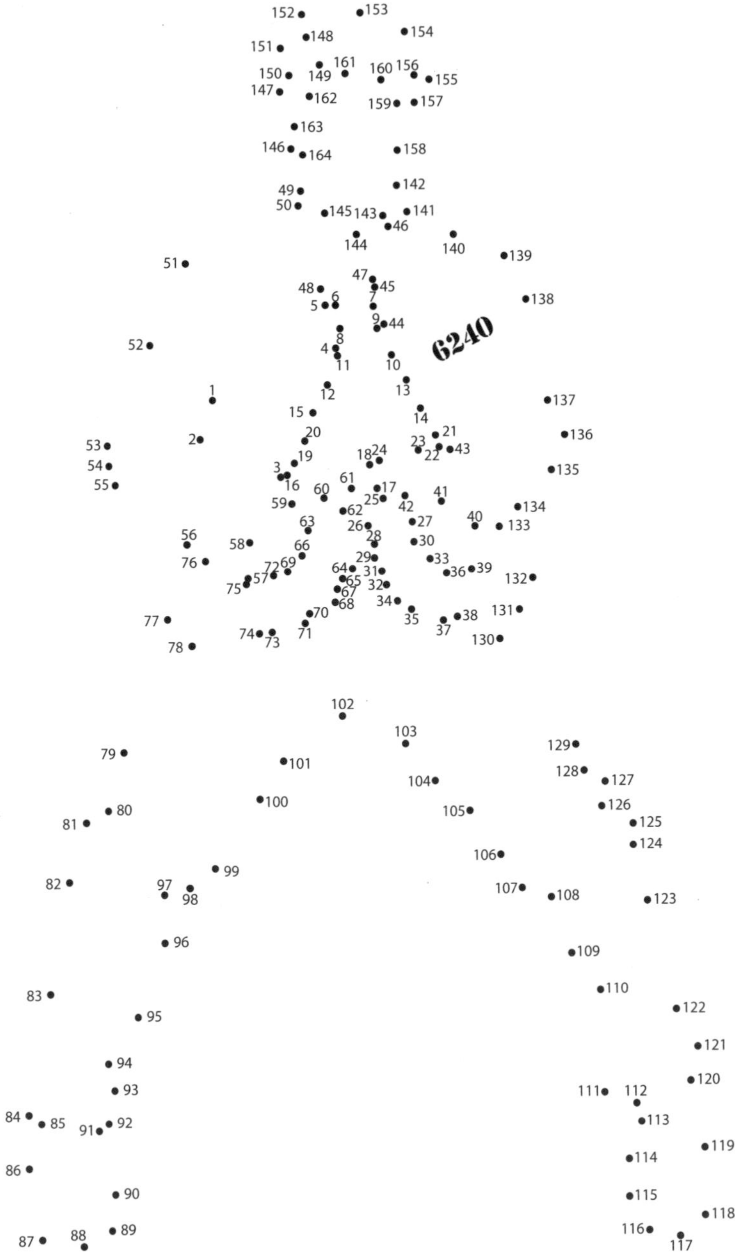

6240

45

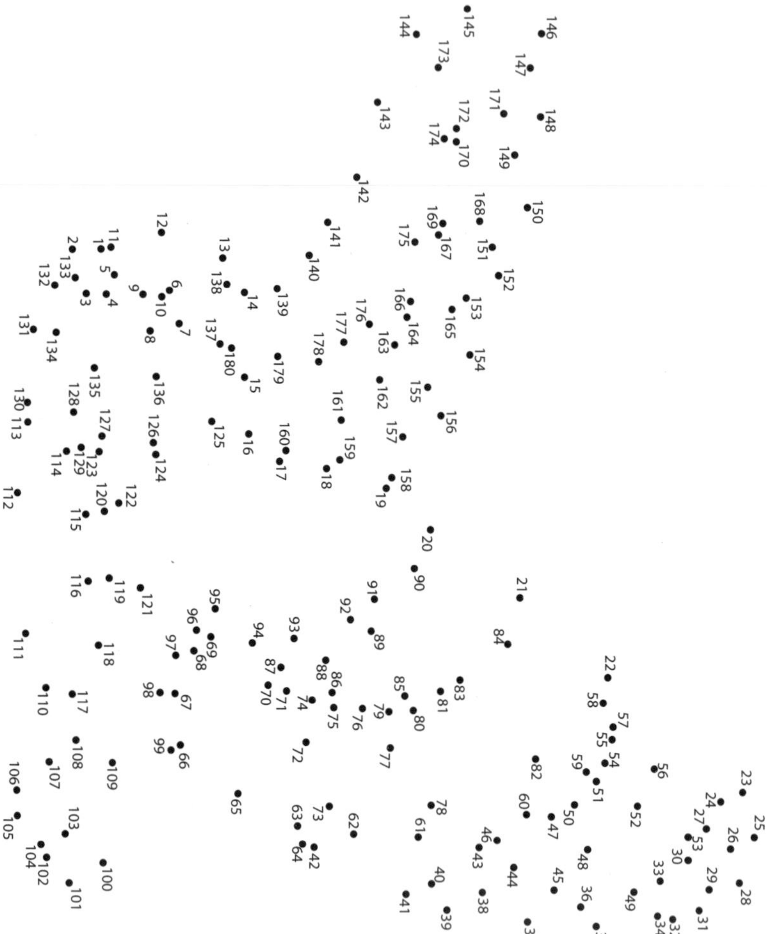

46

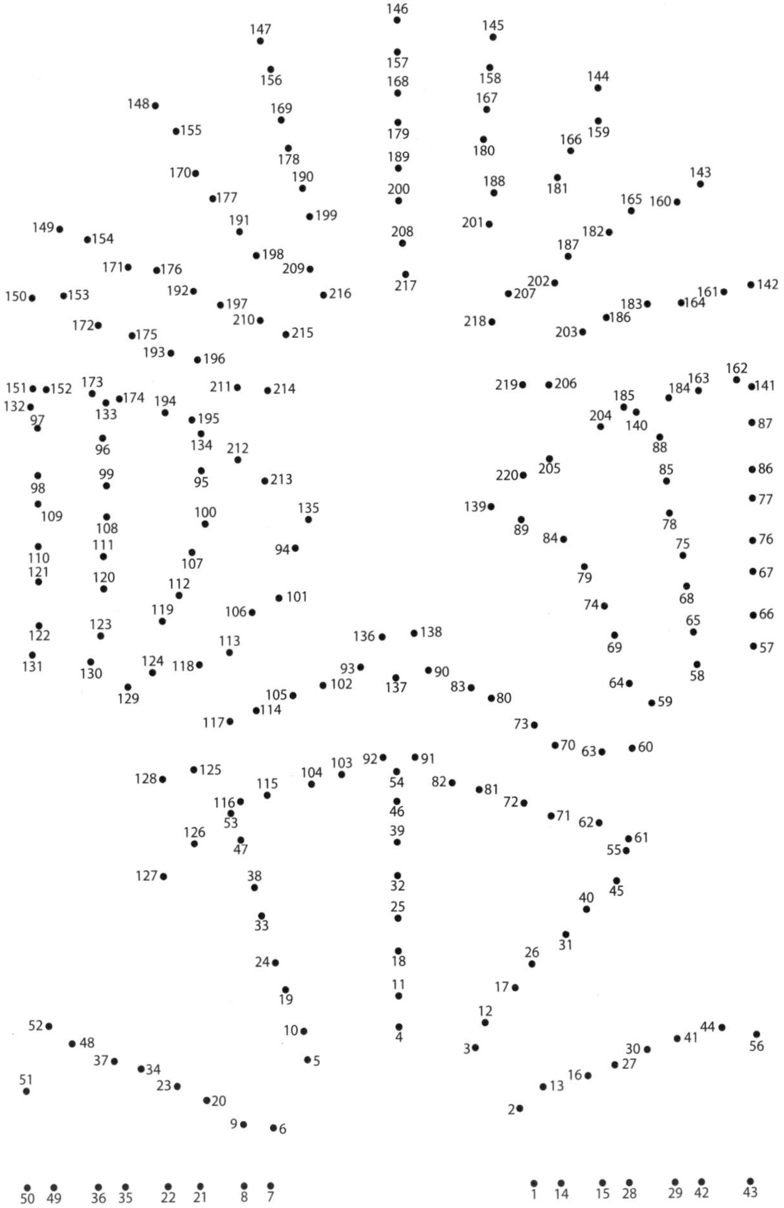

47

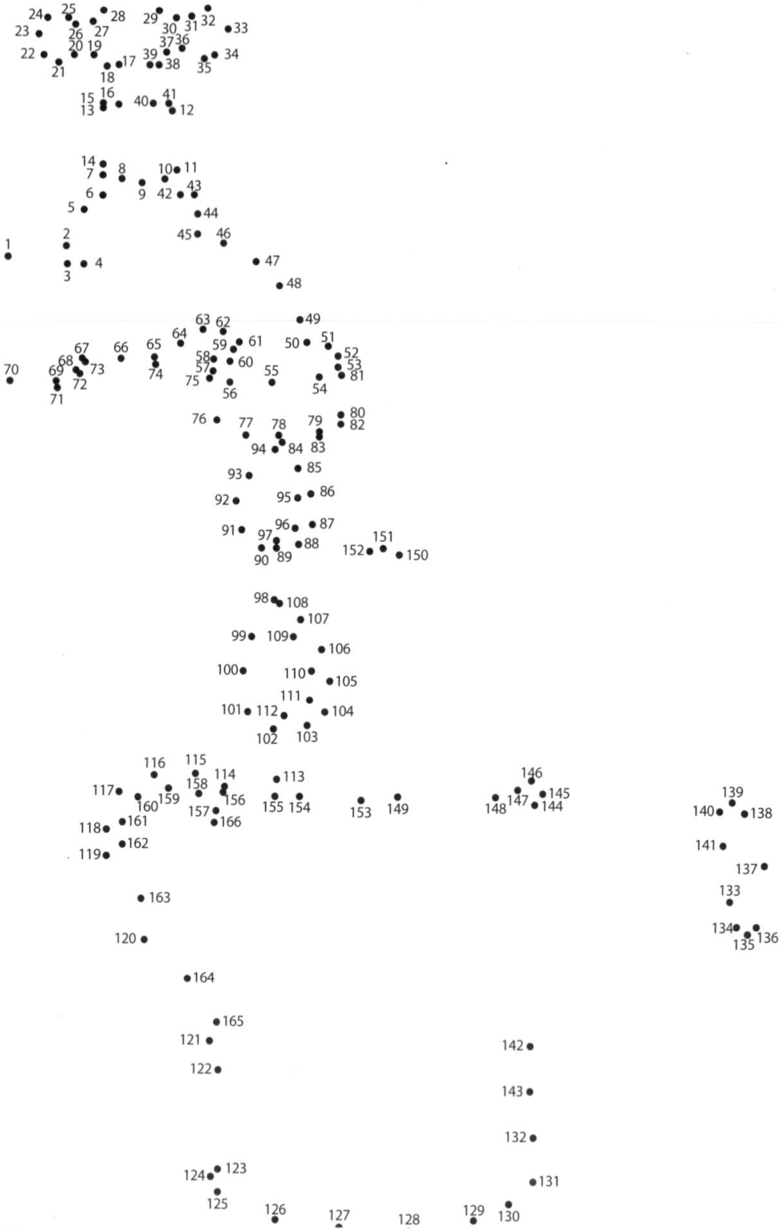

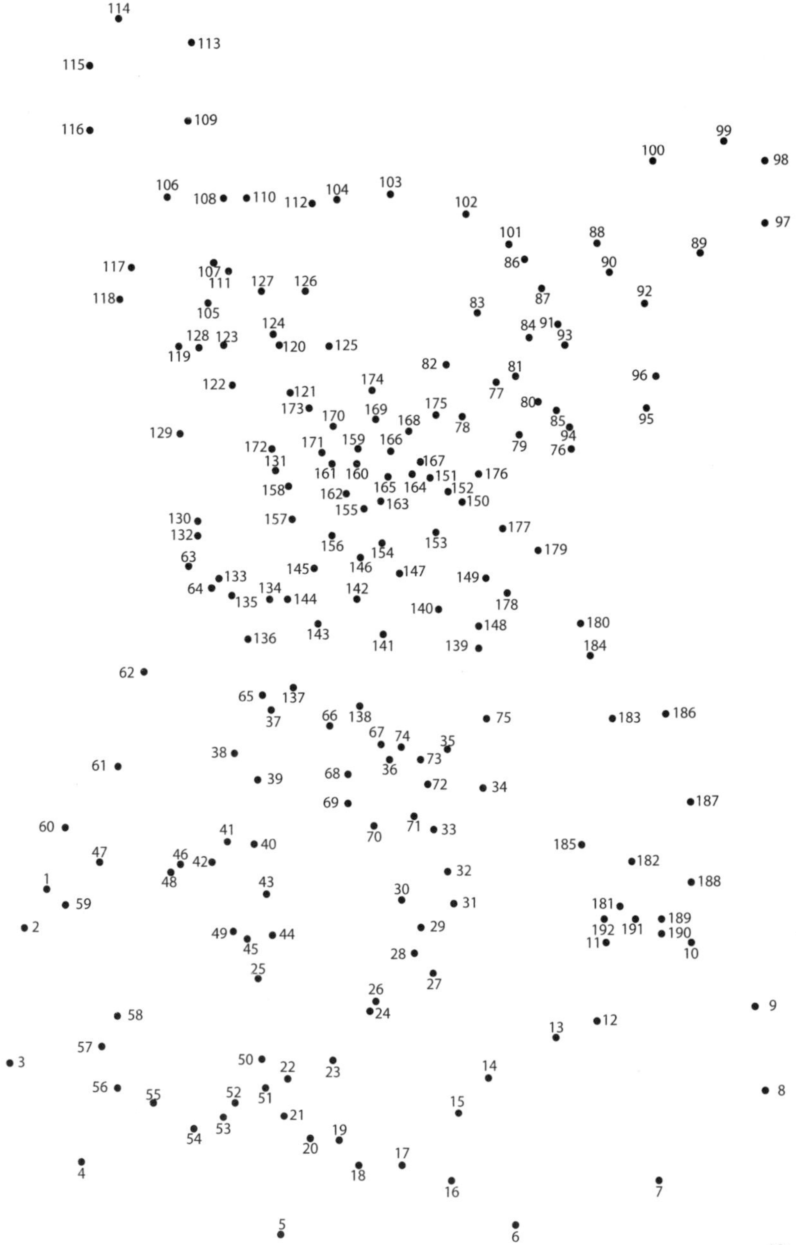

49

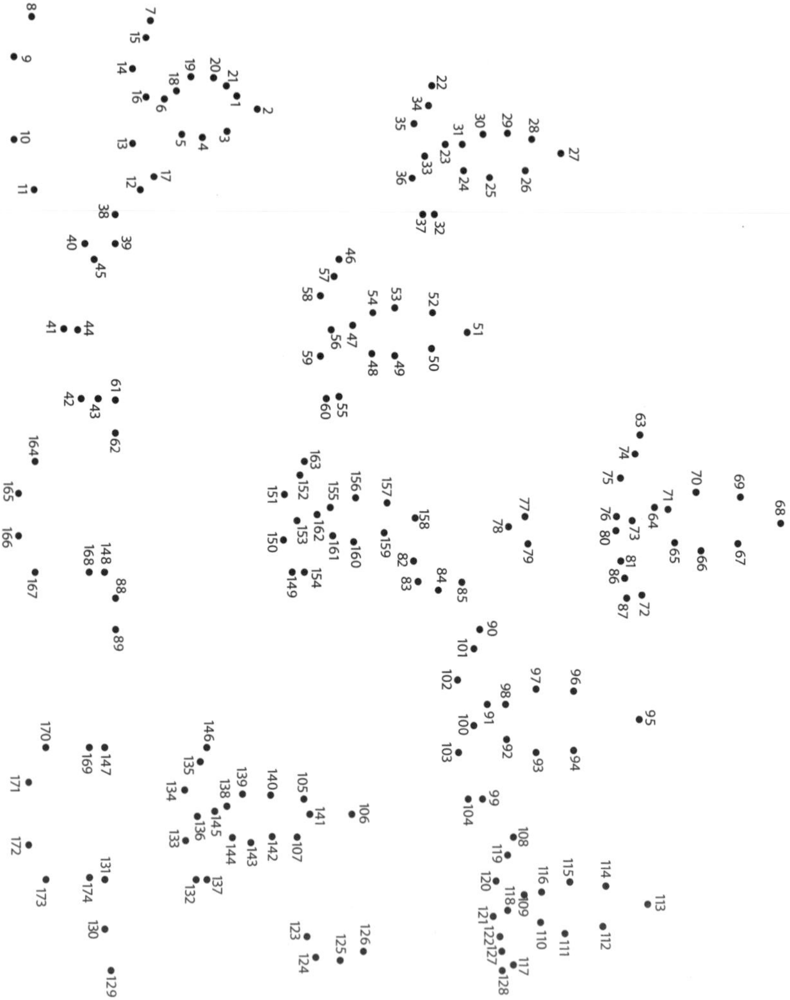

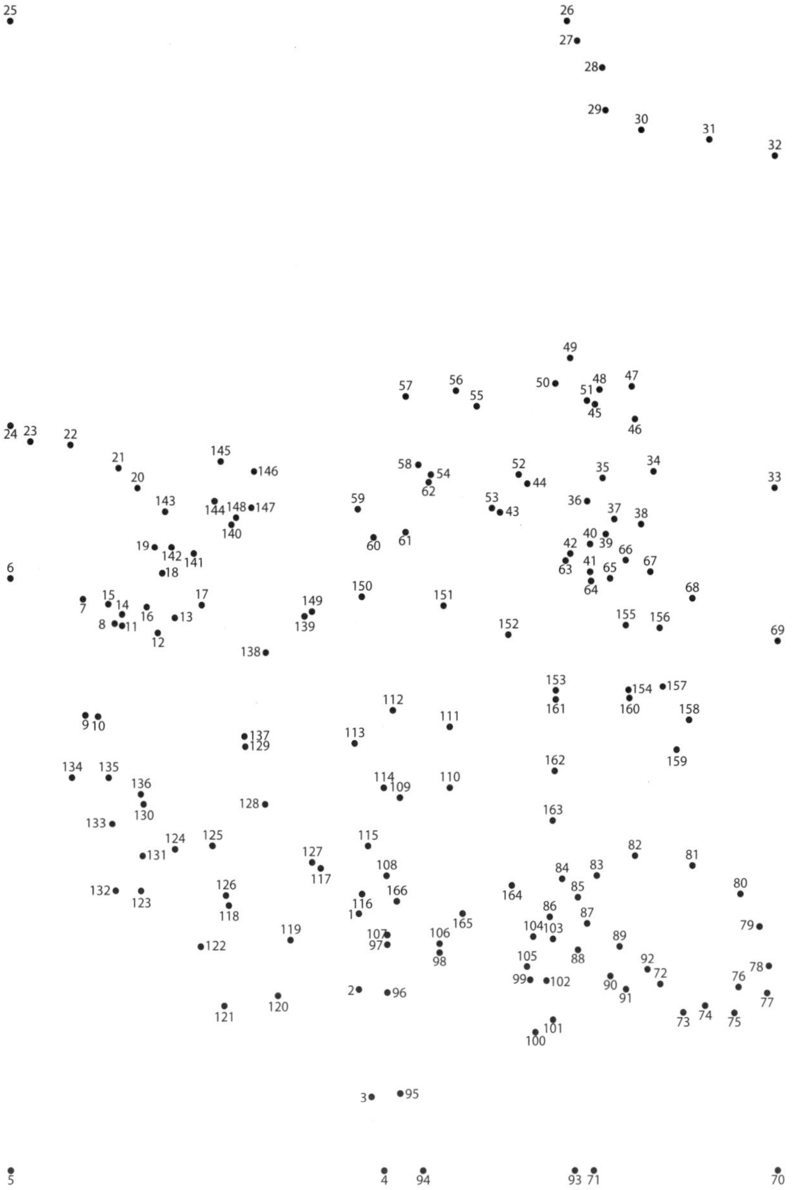

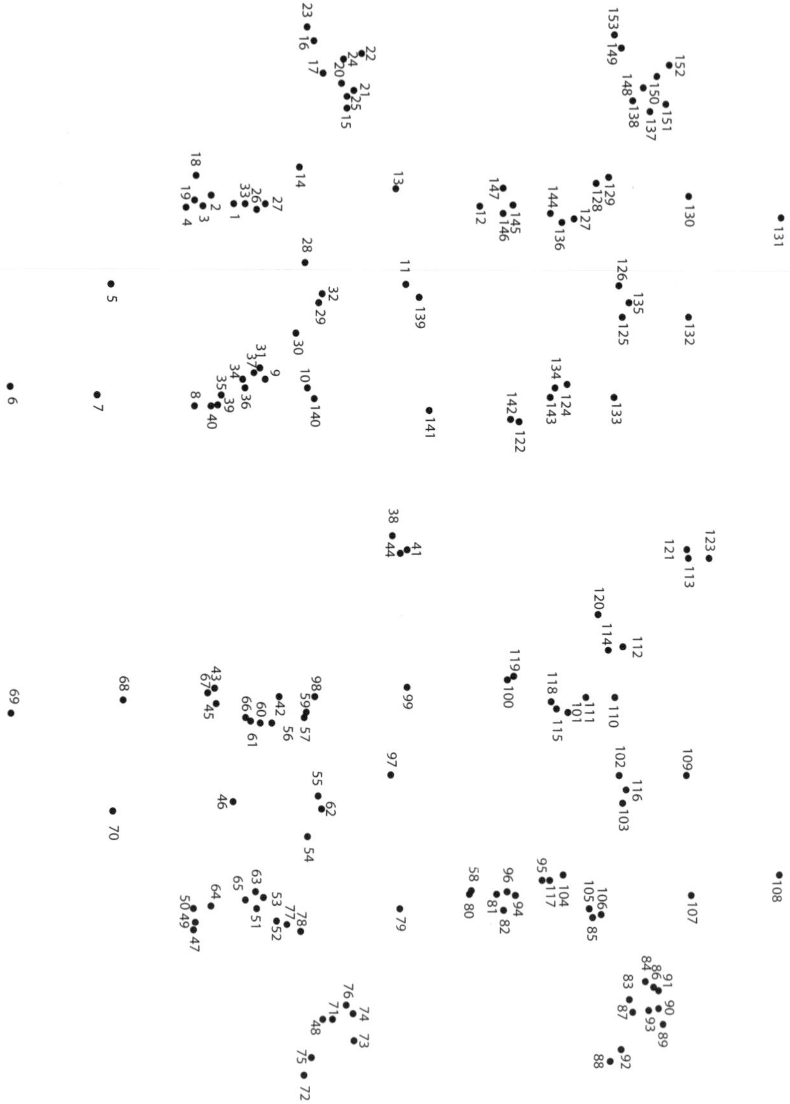

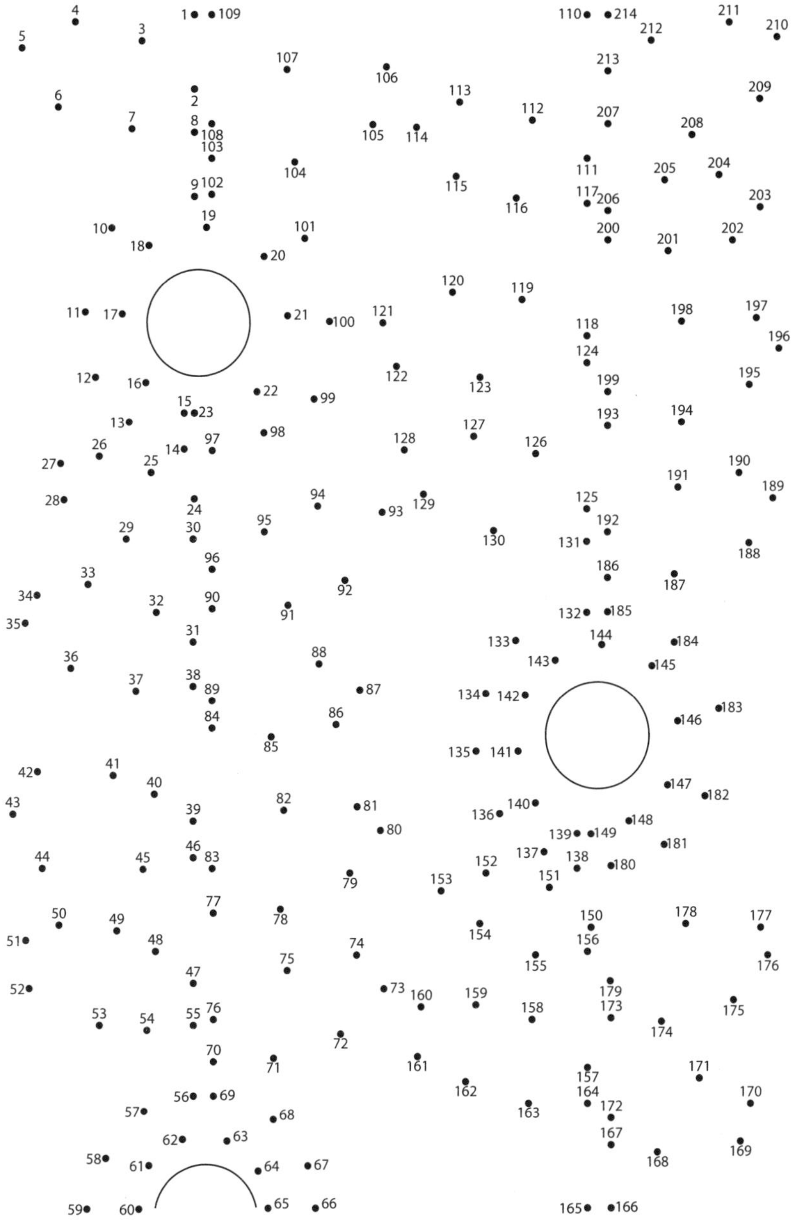

53

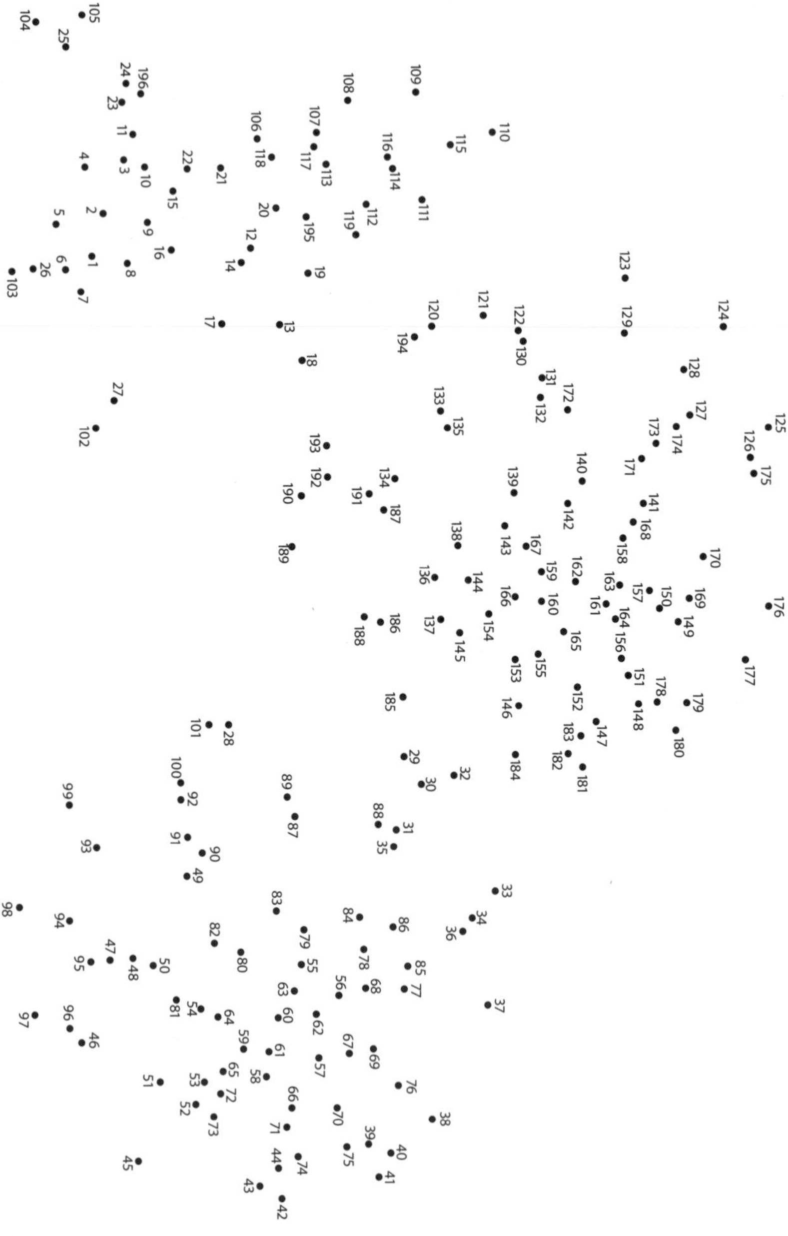

54

55

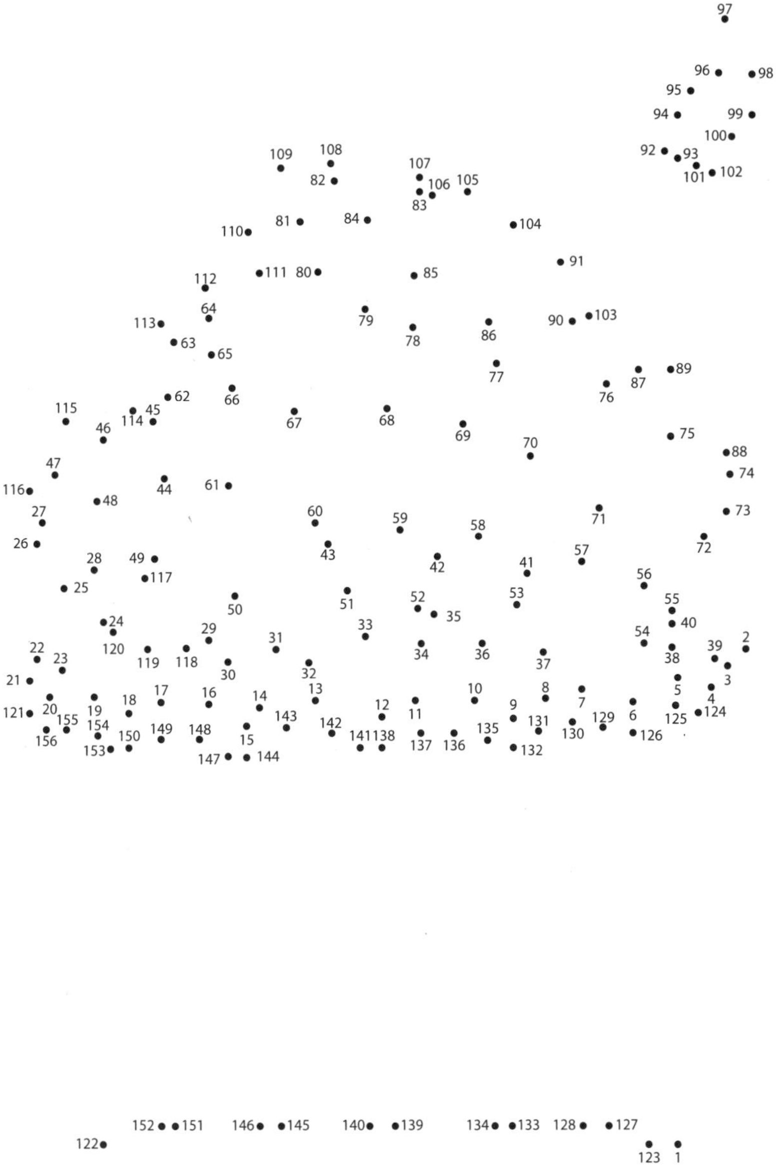

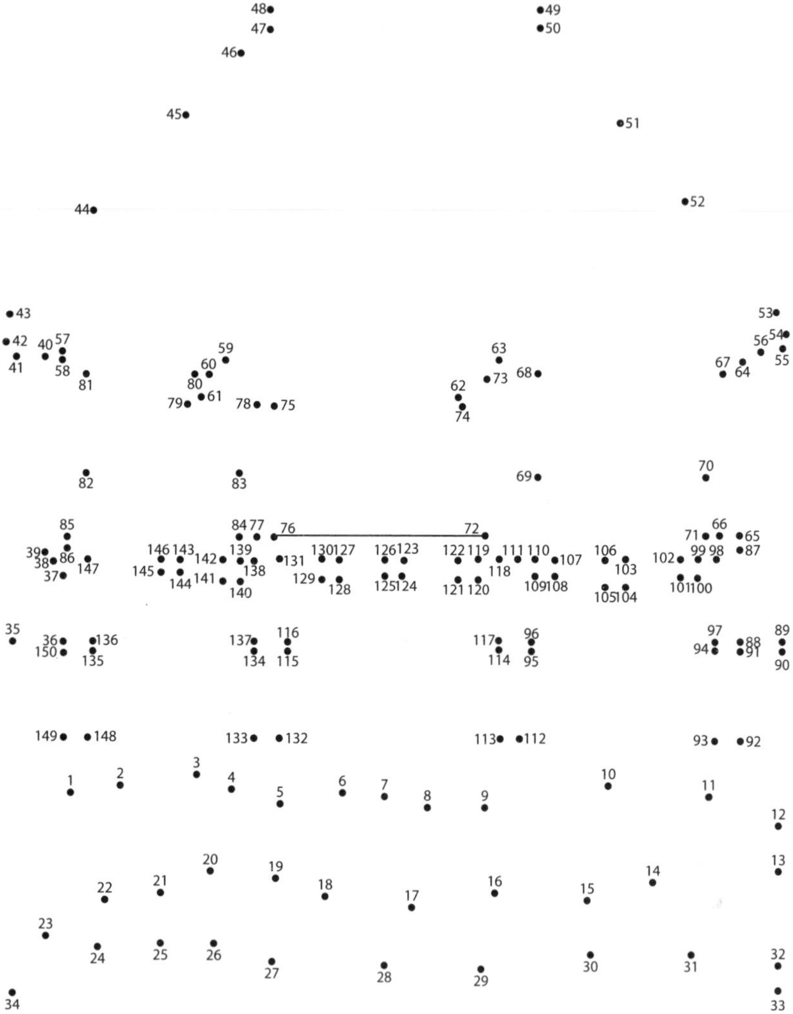

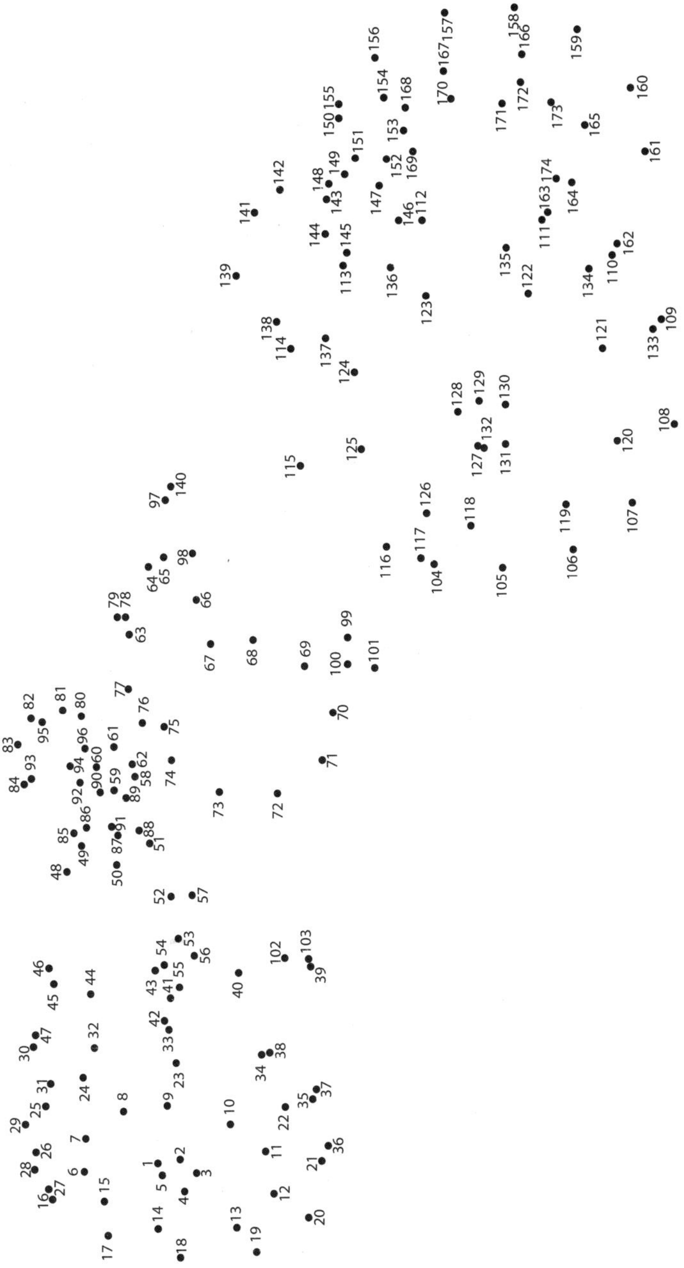

57

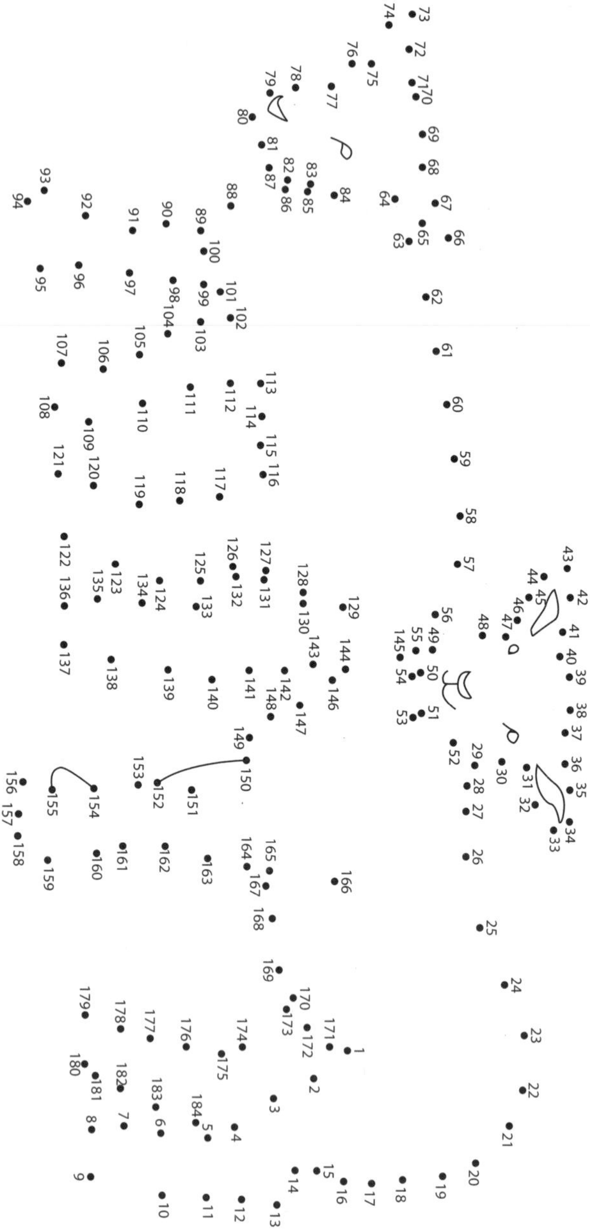

58

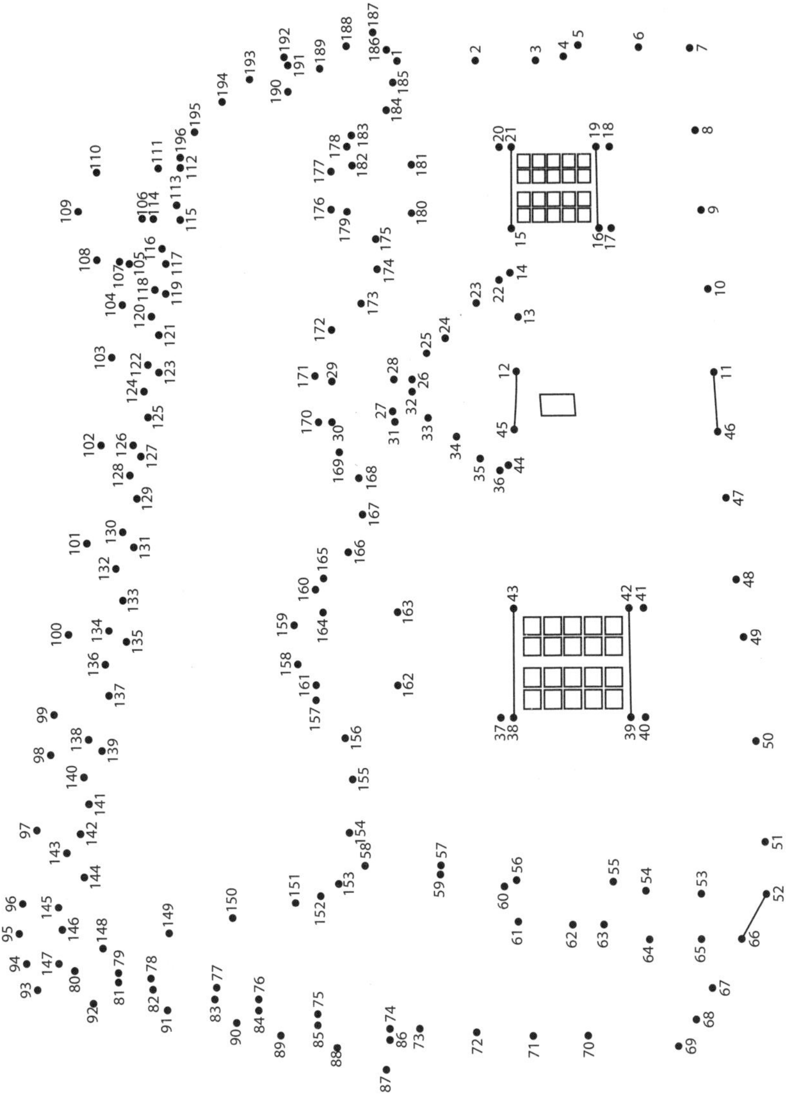

59

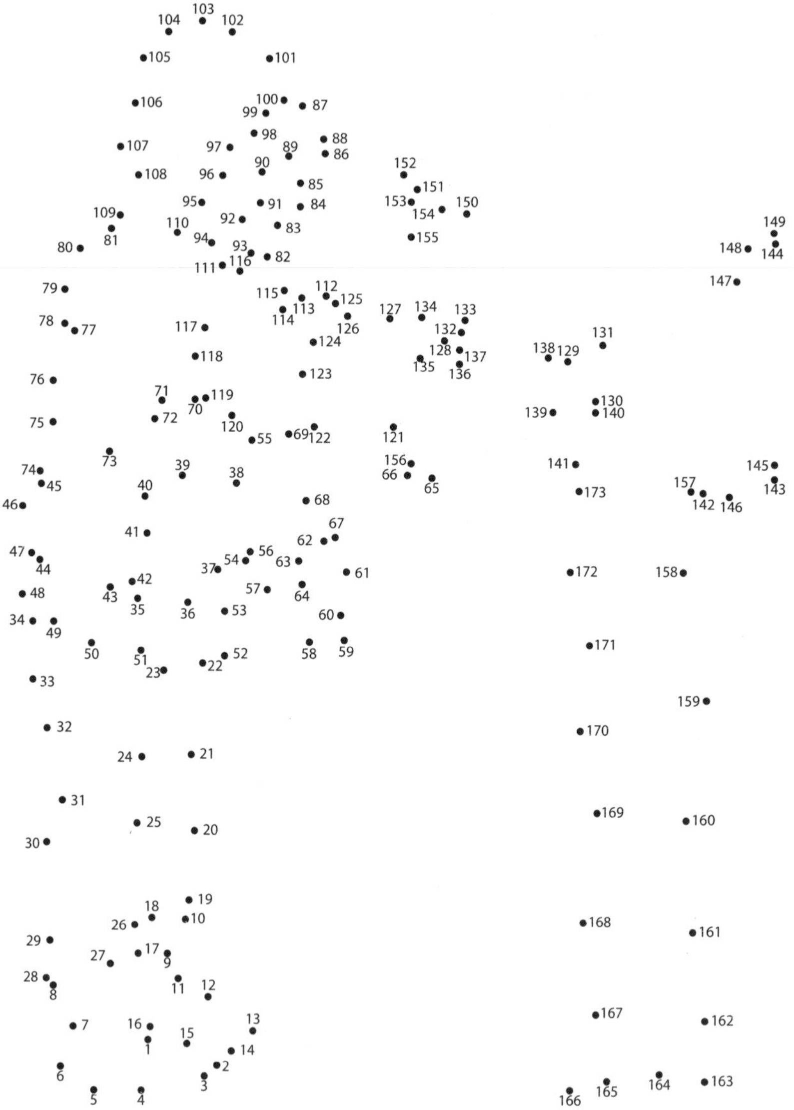

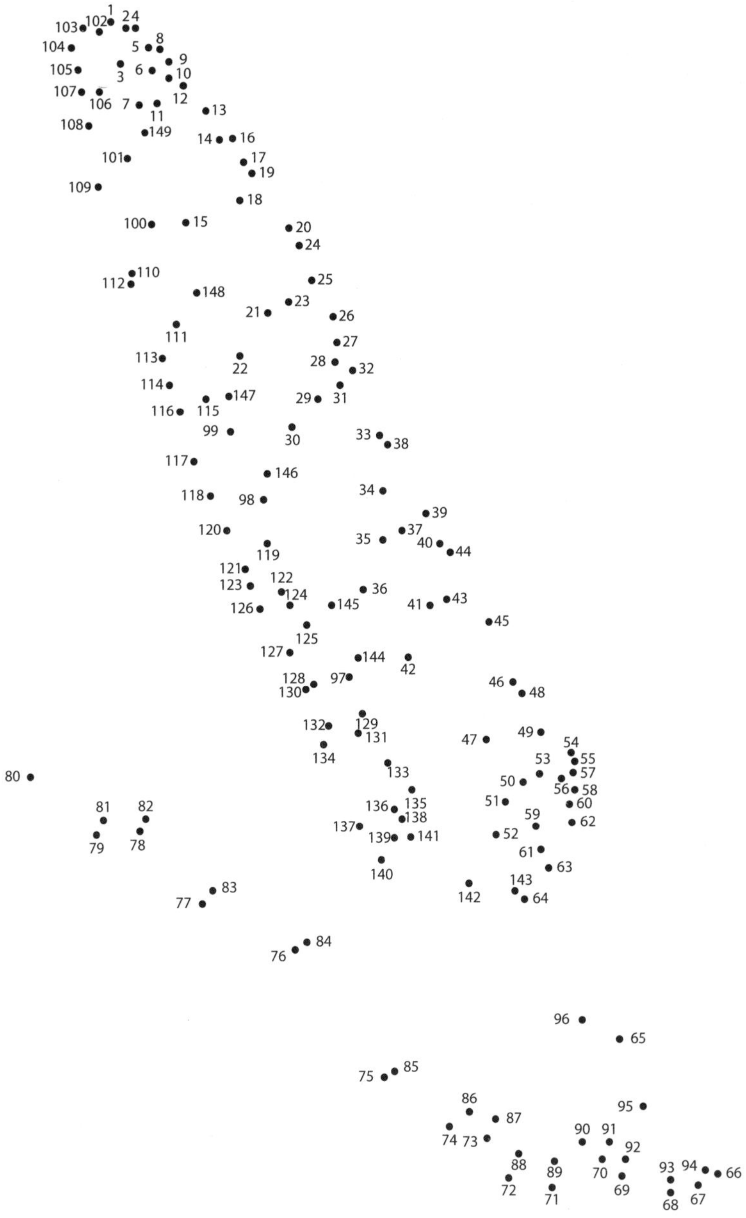

61

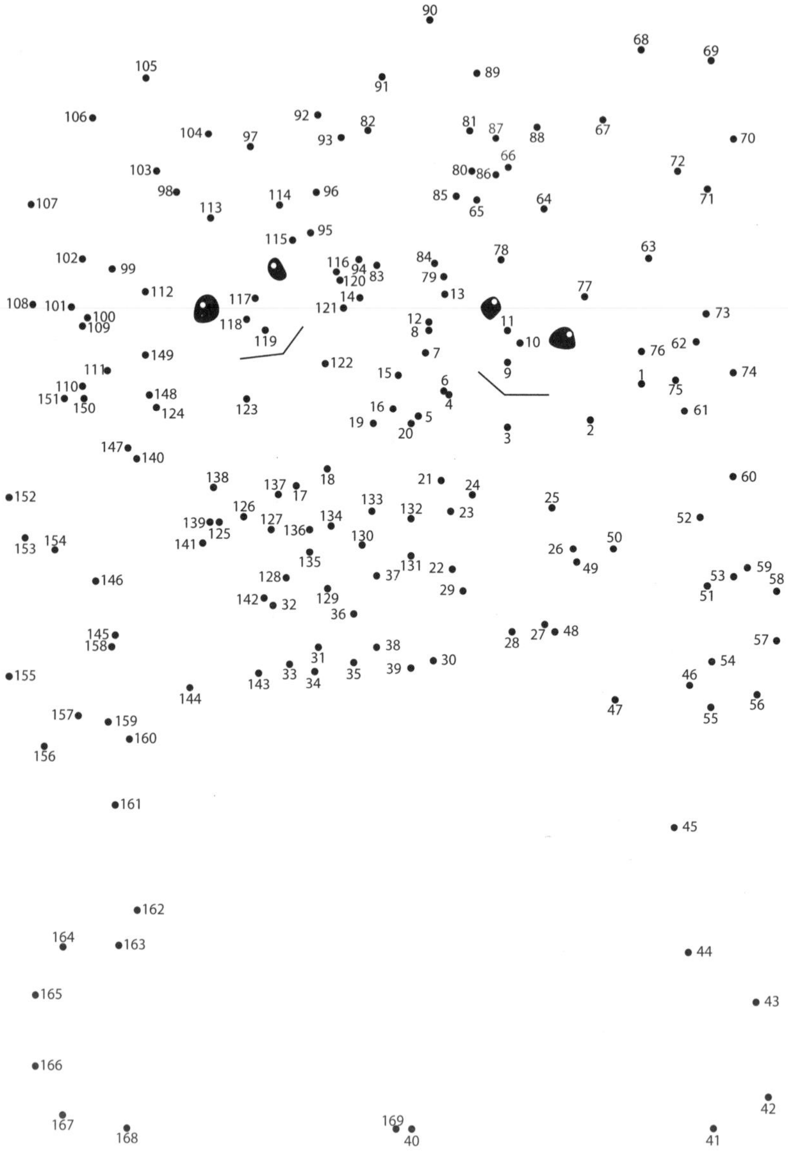

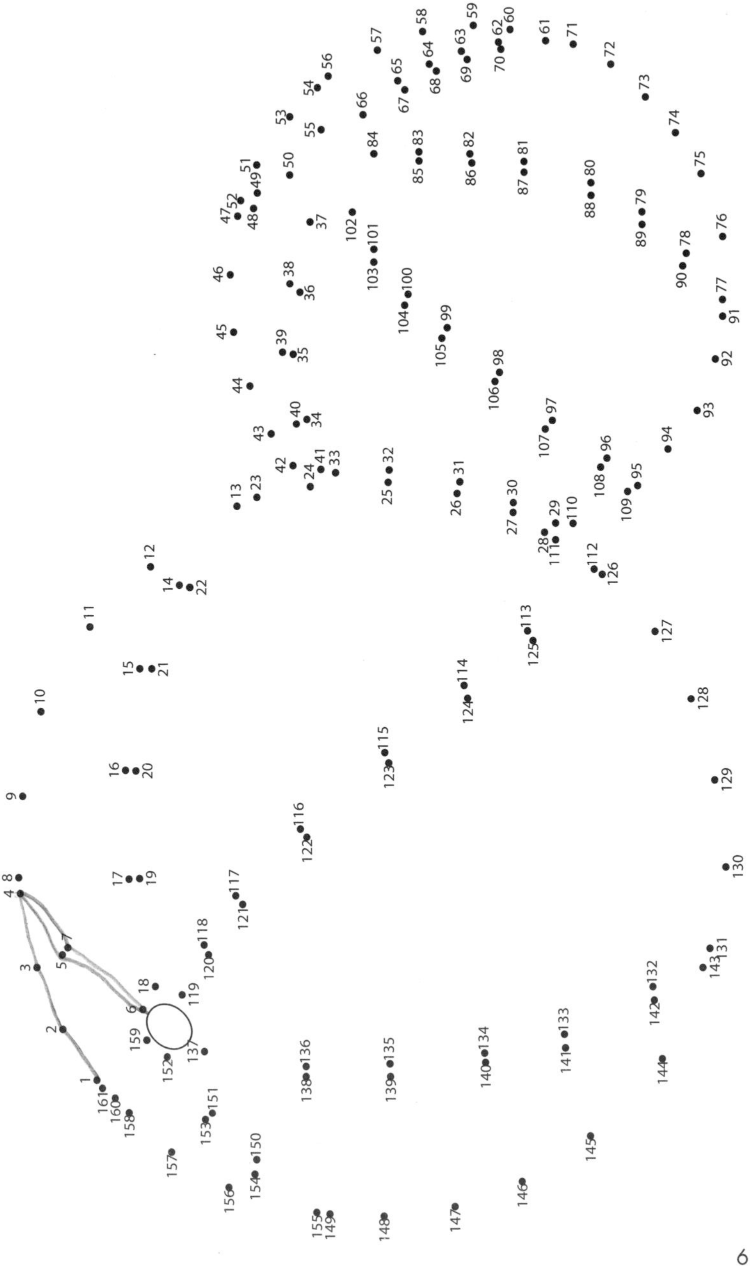

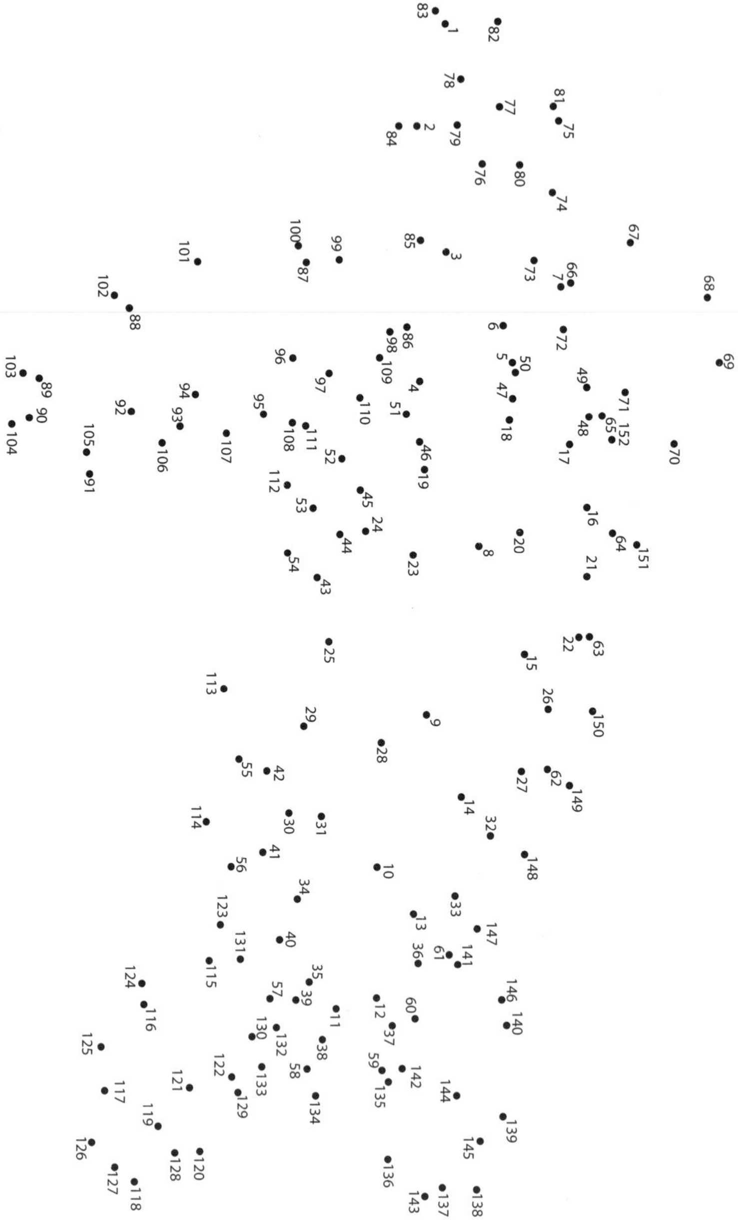

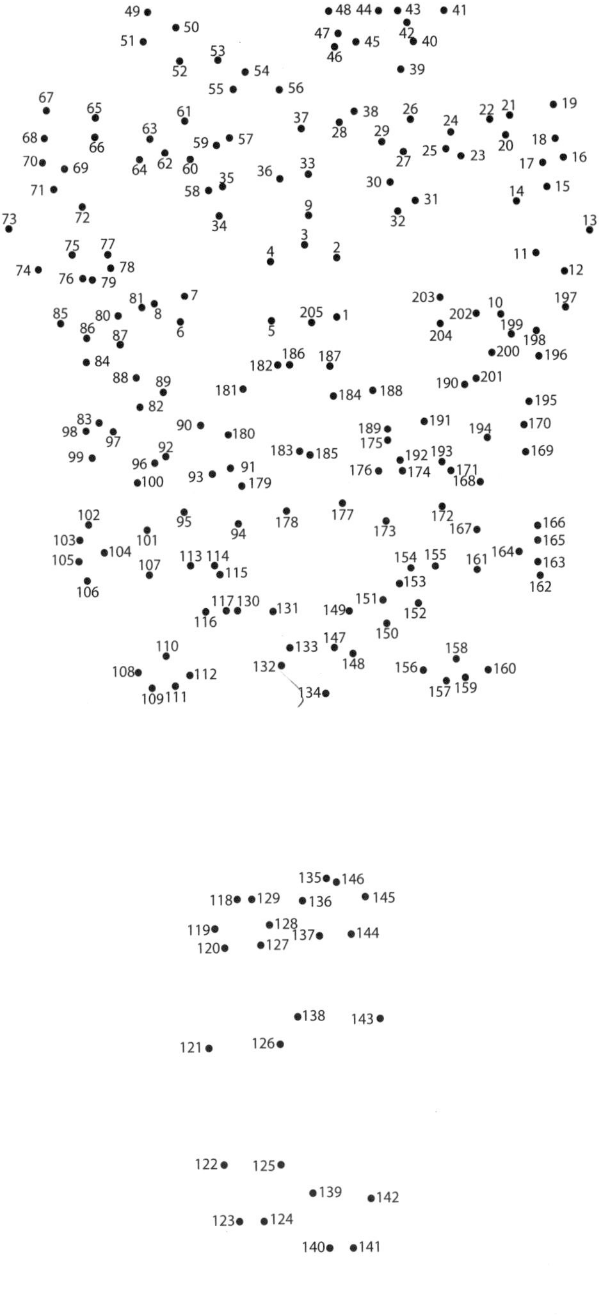

65

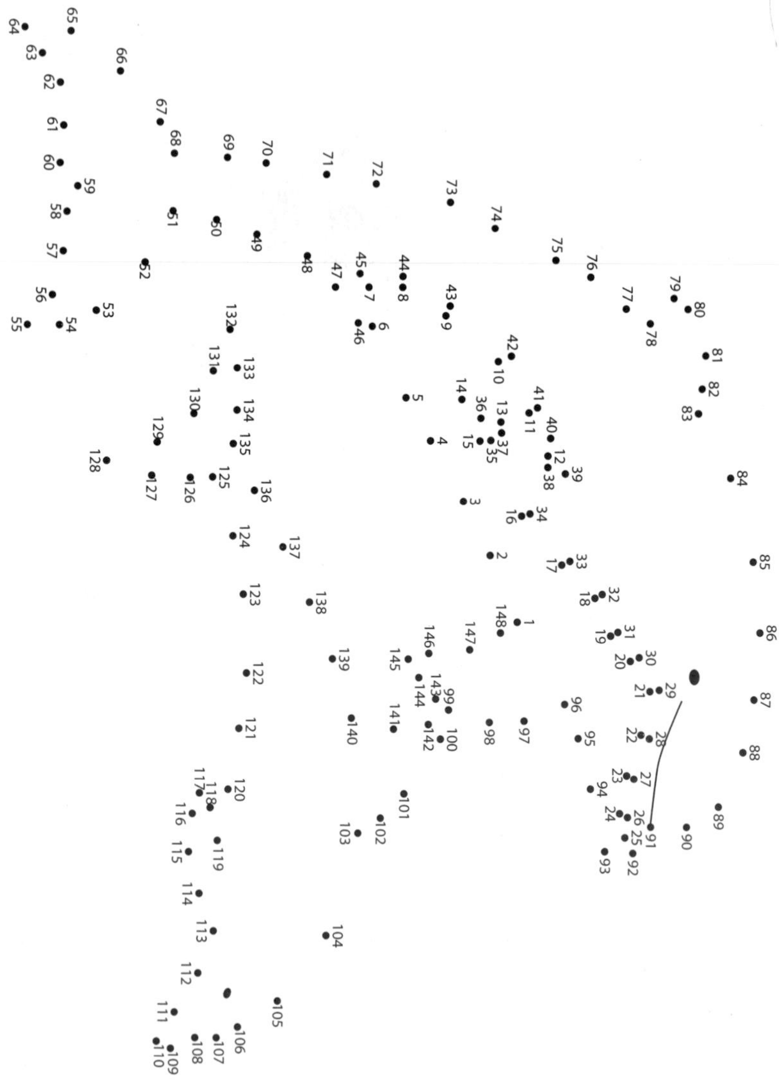

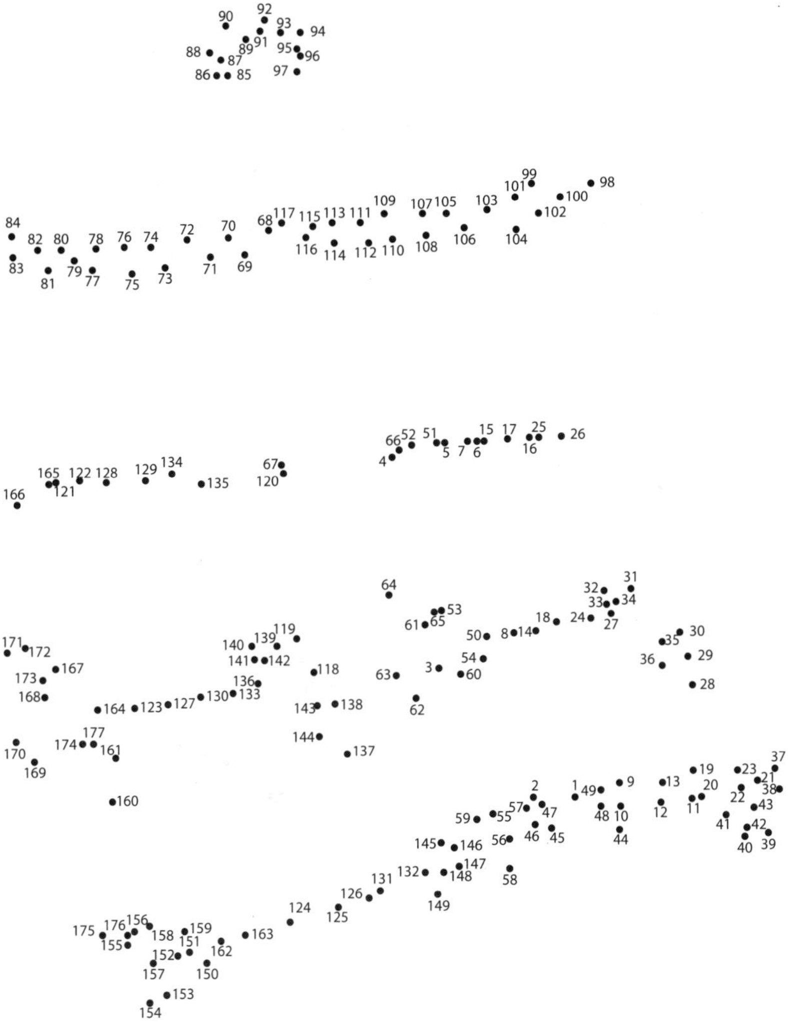

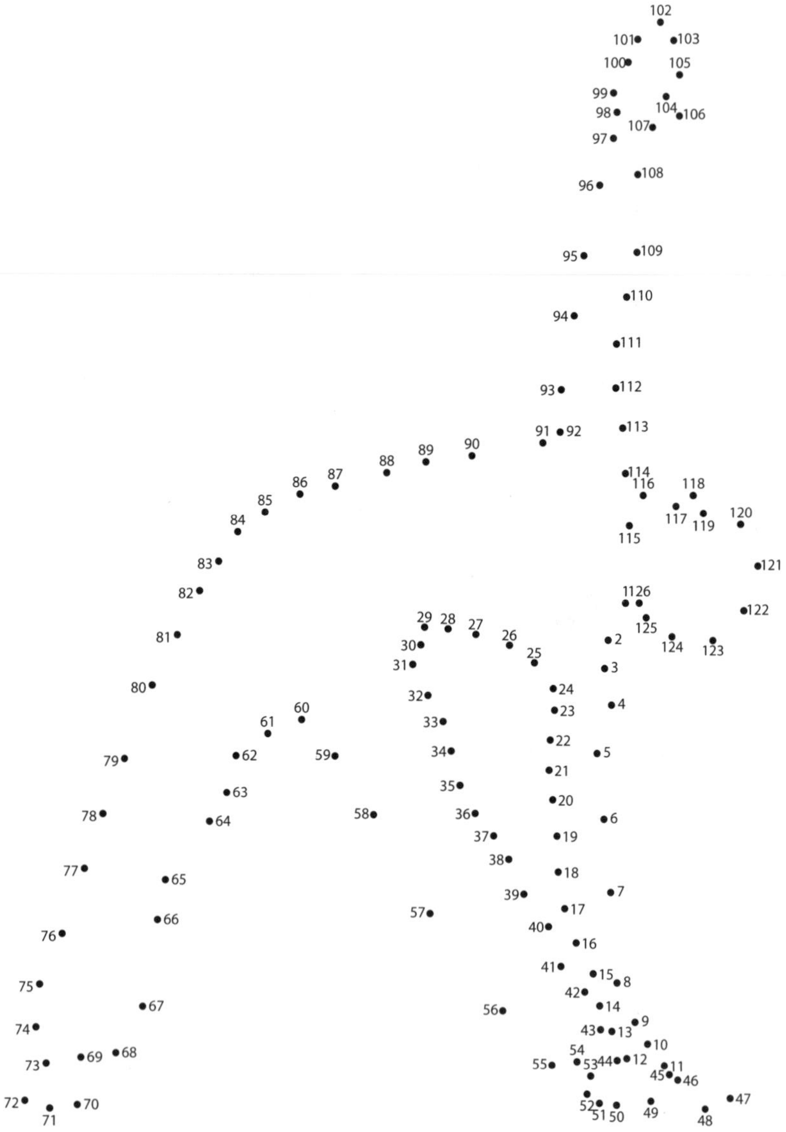

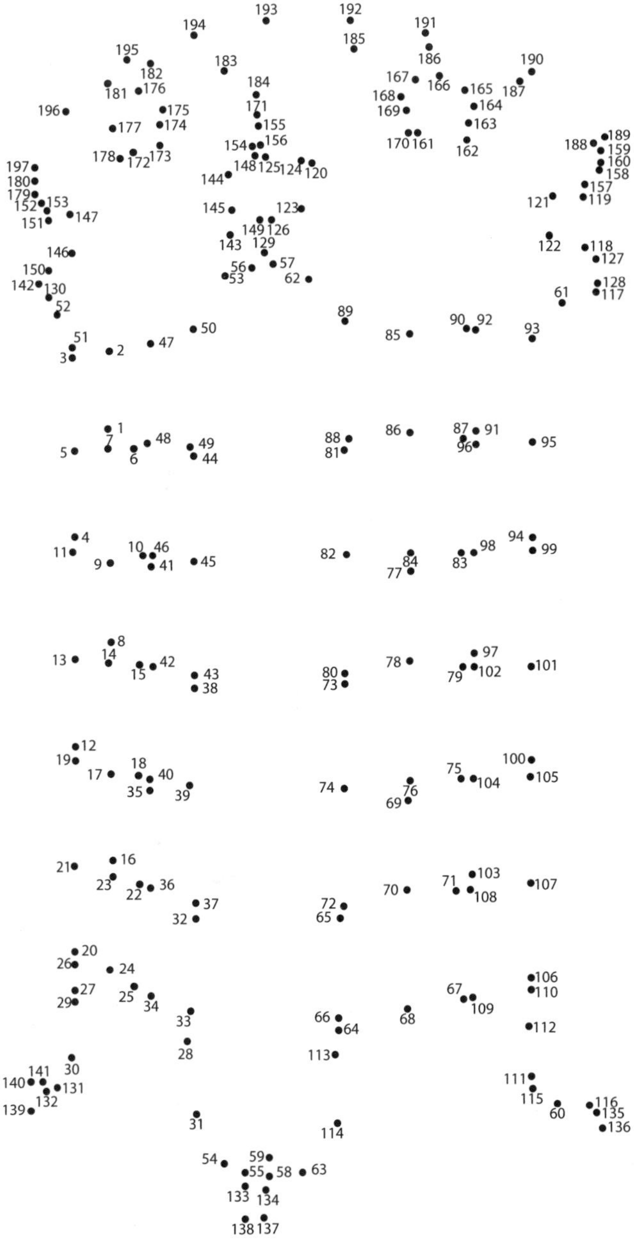

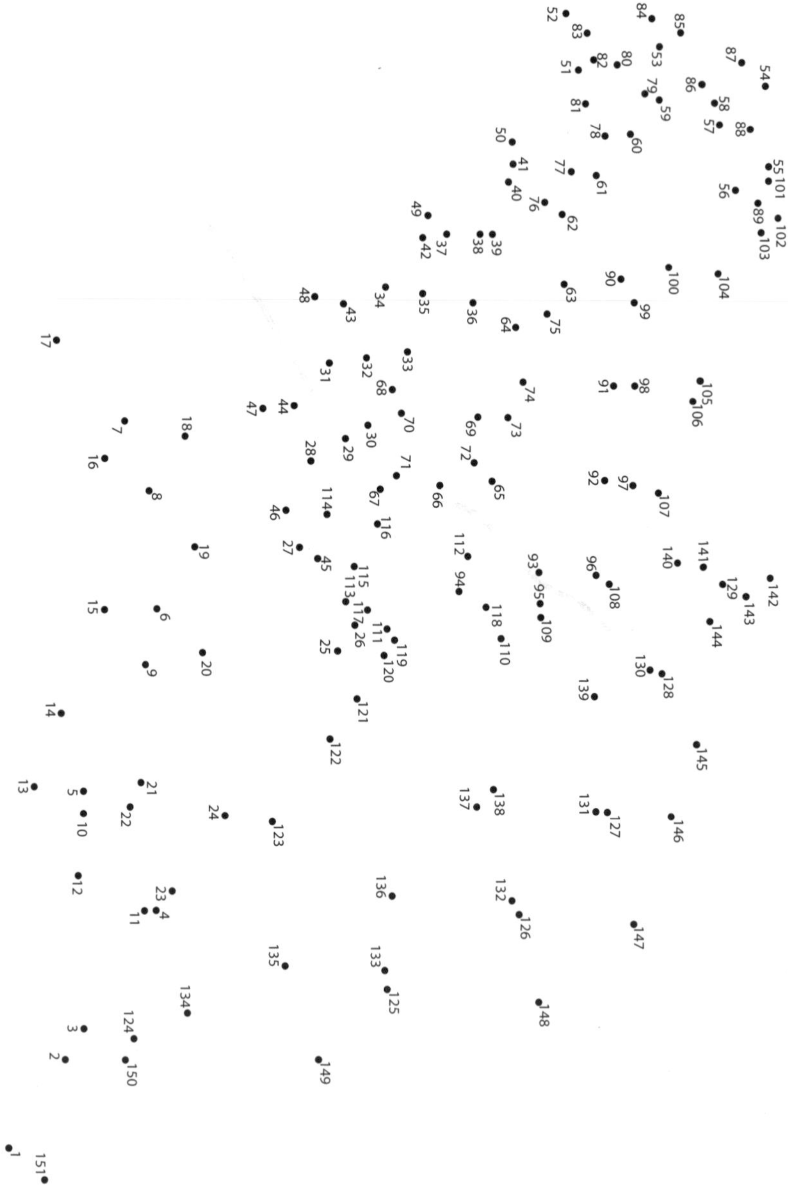

72

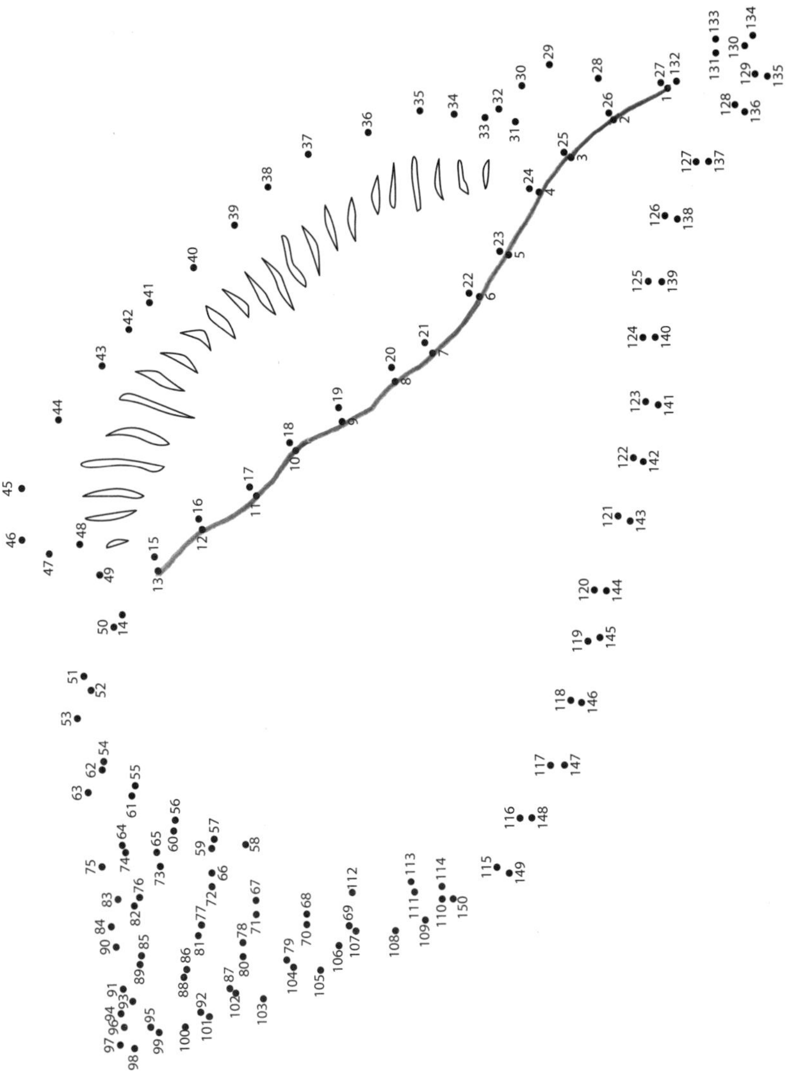

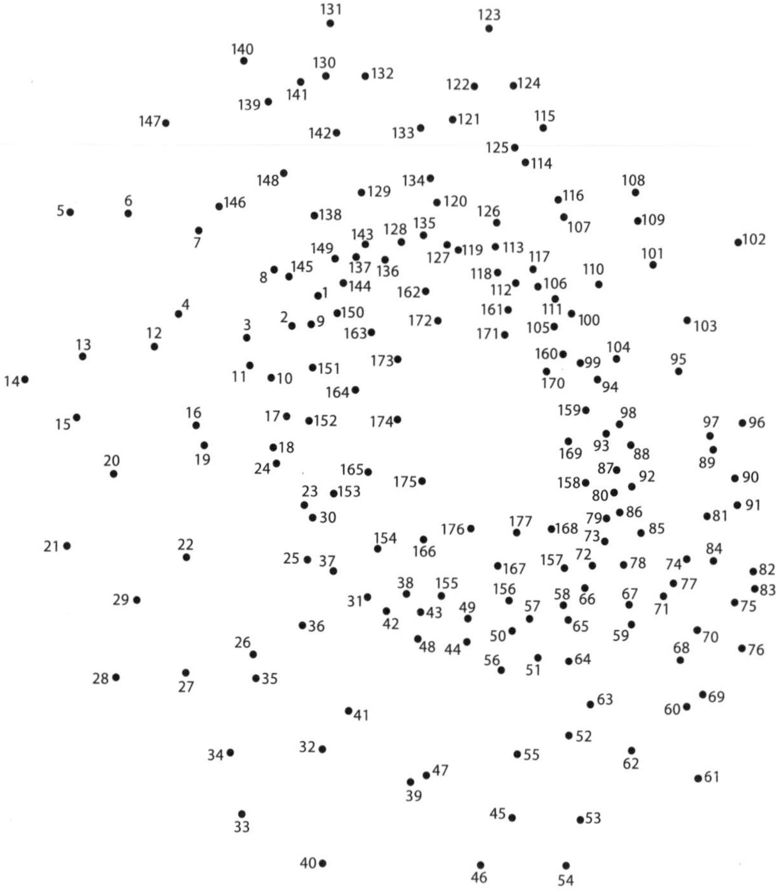

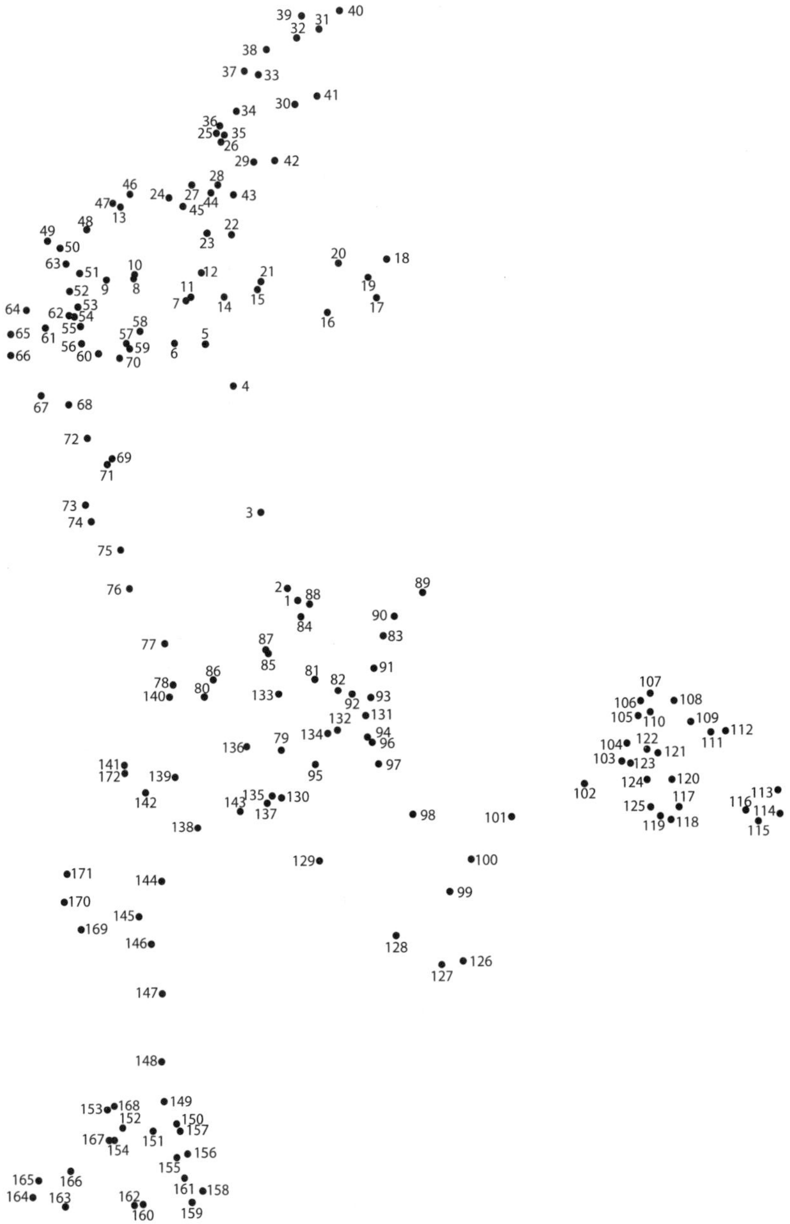

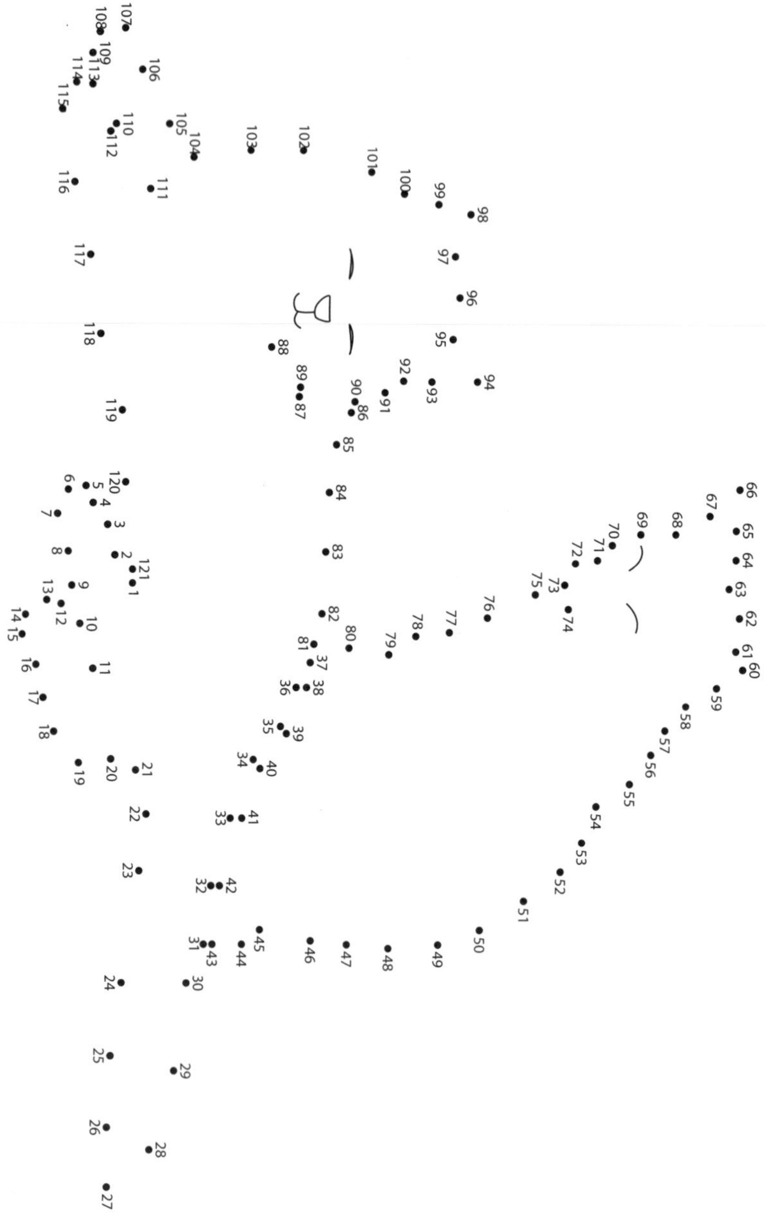

76

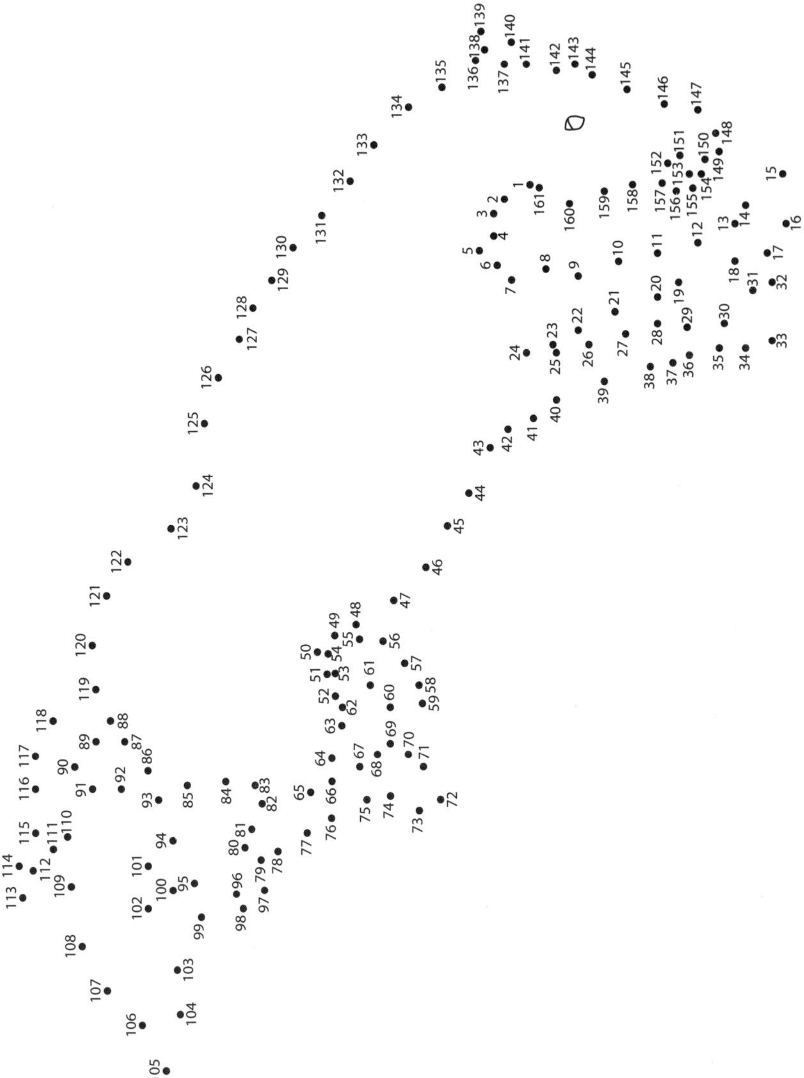

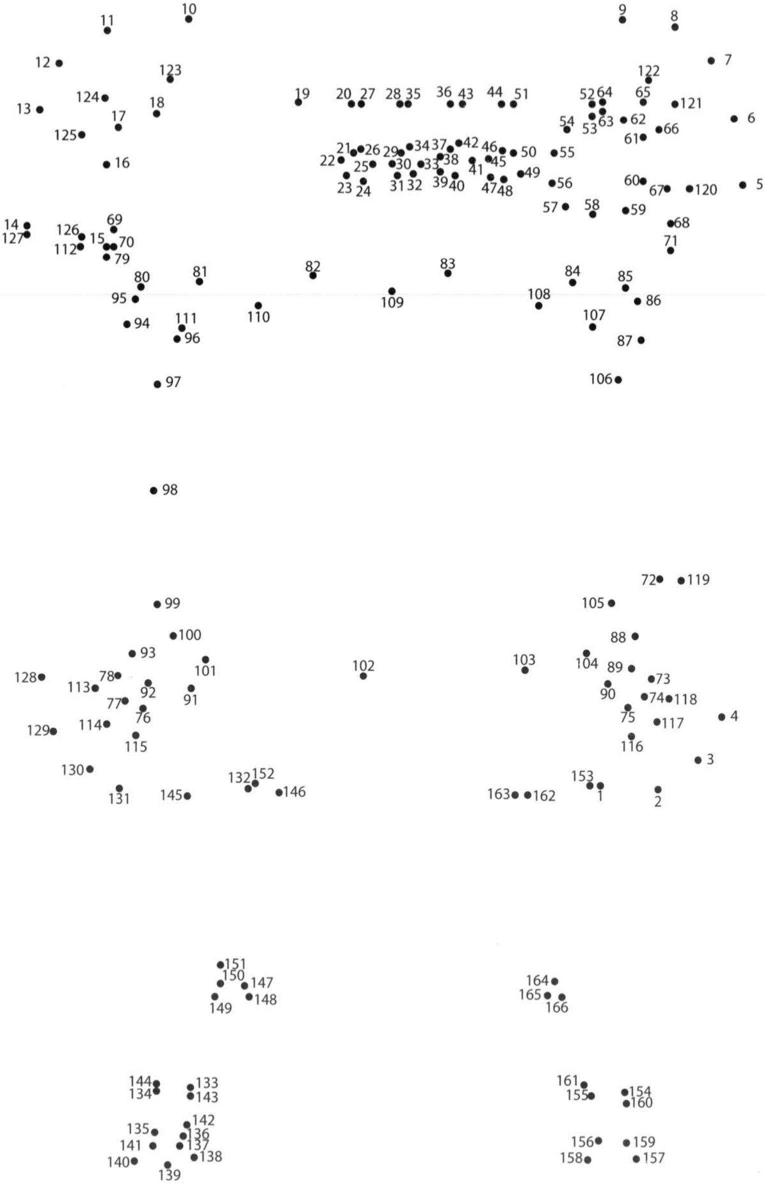

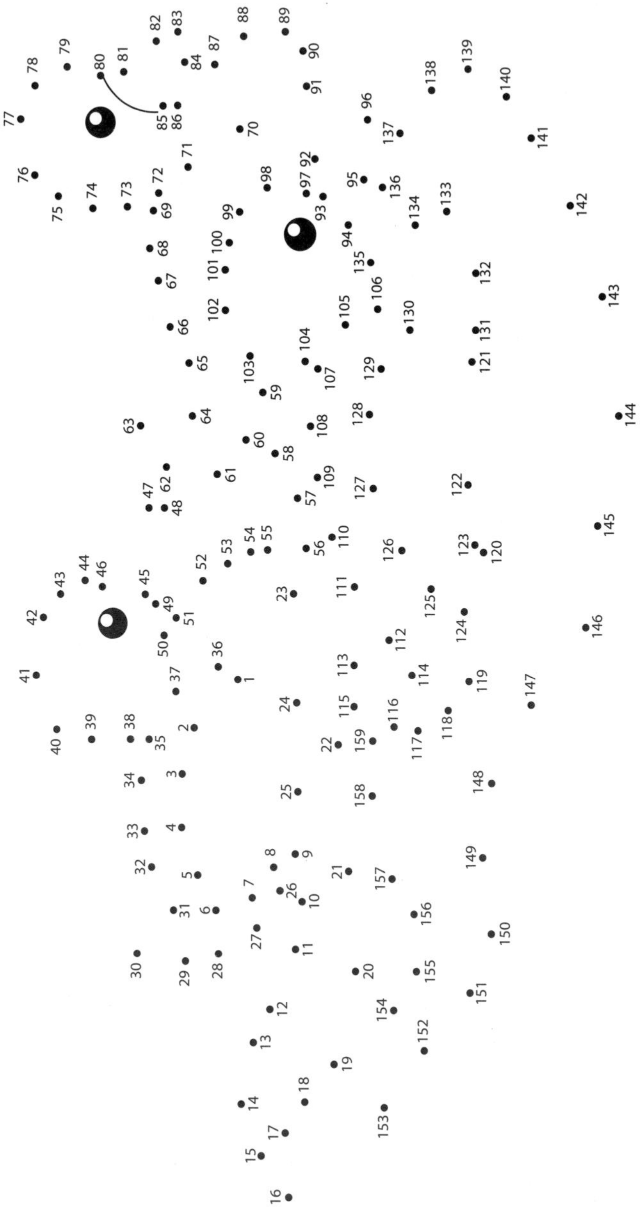

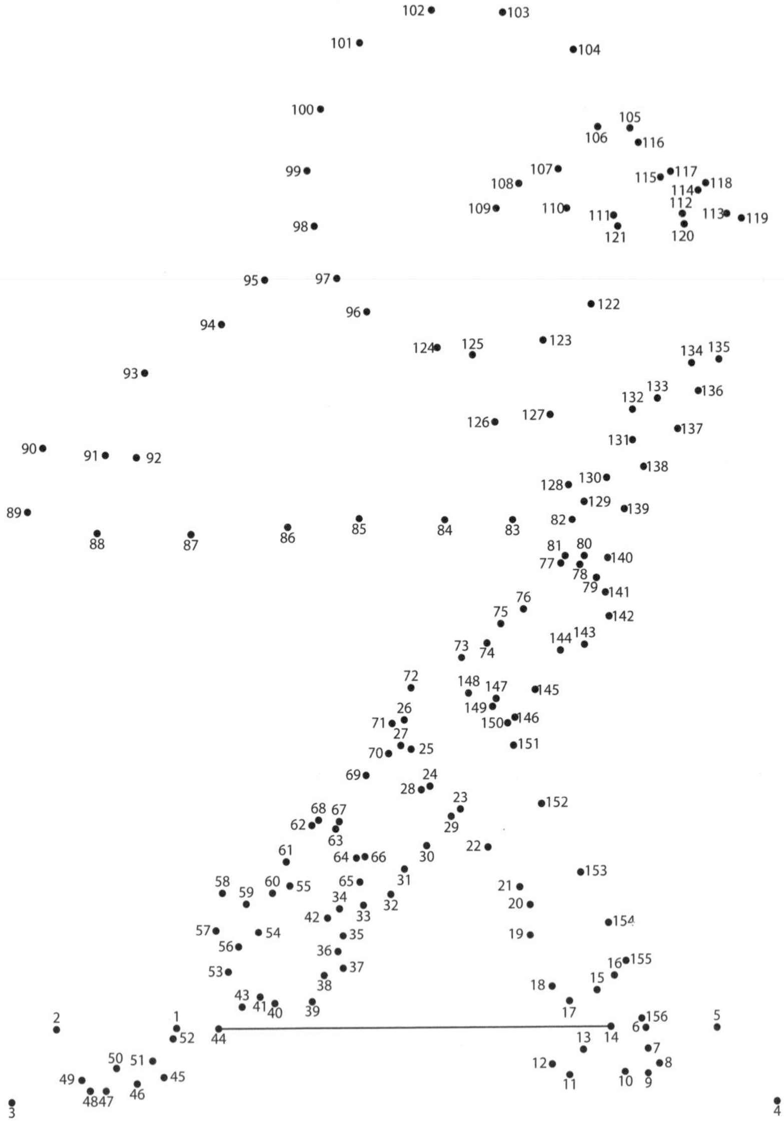

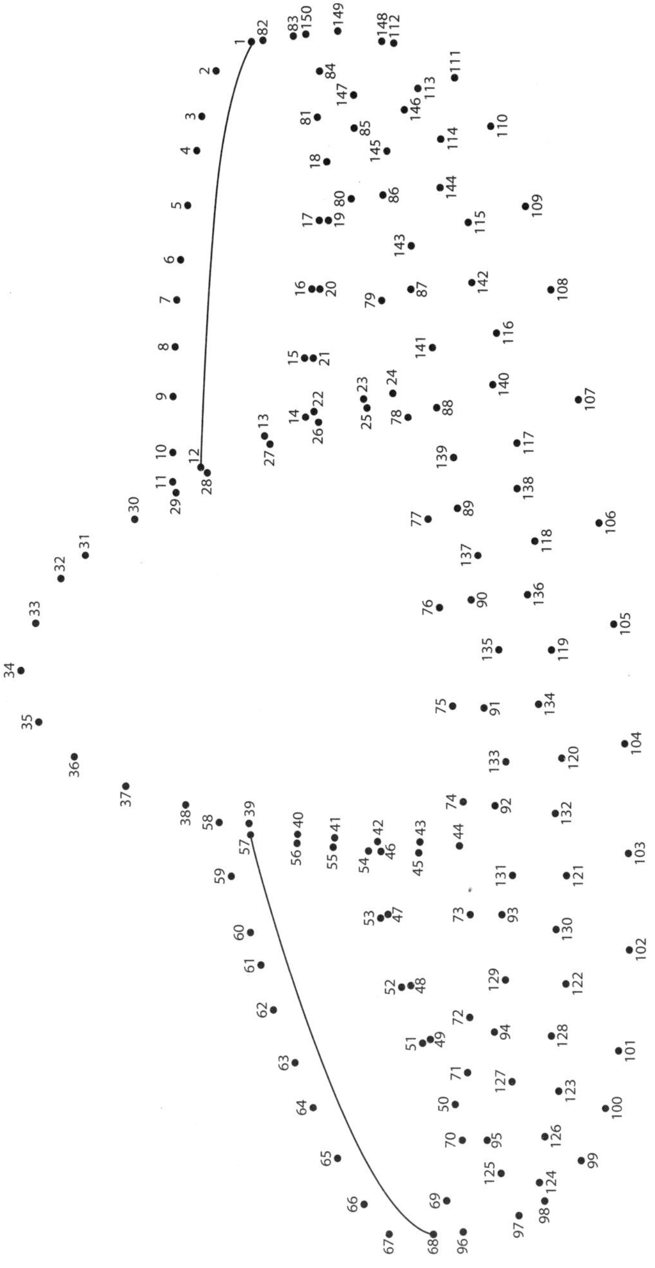

81

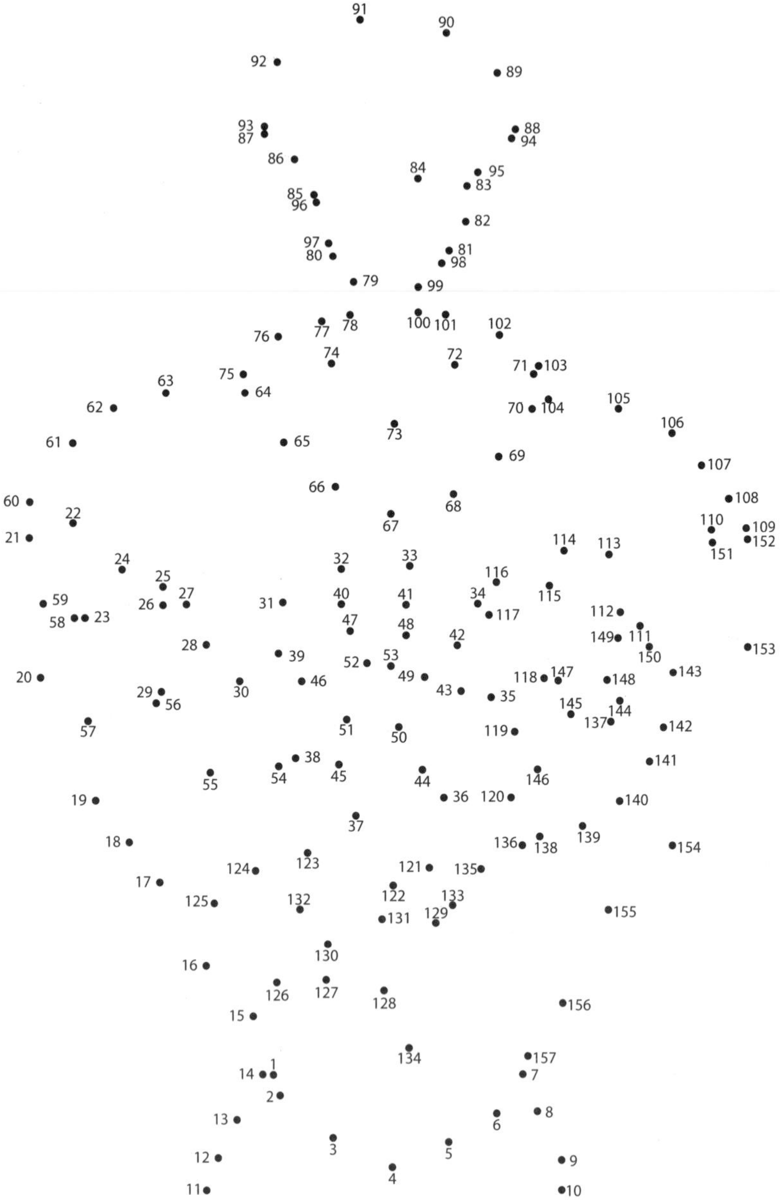

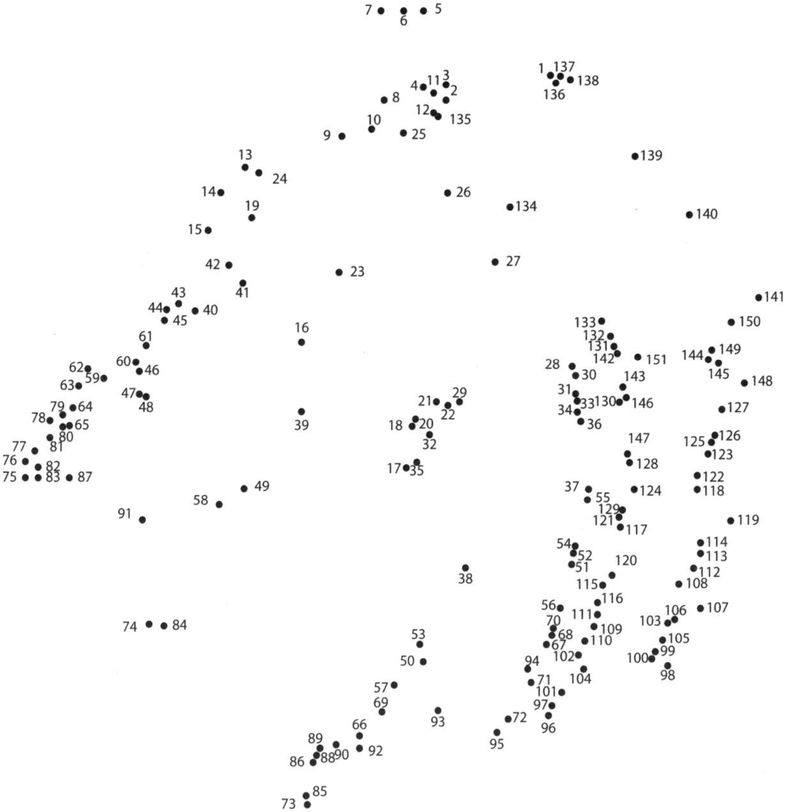

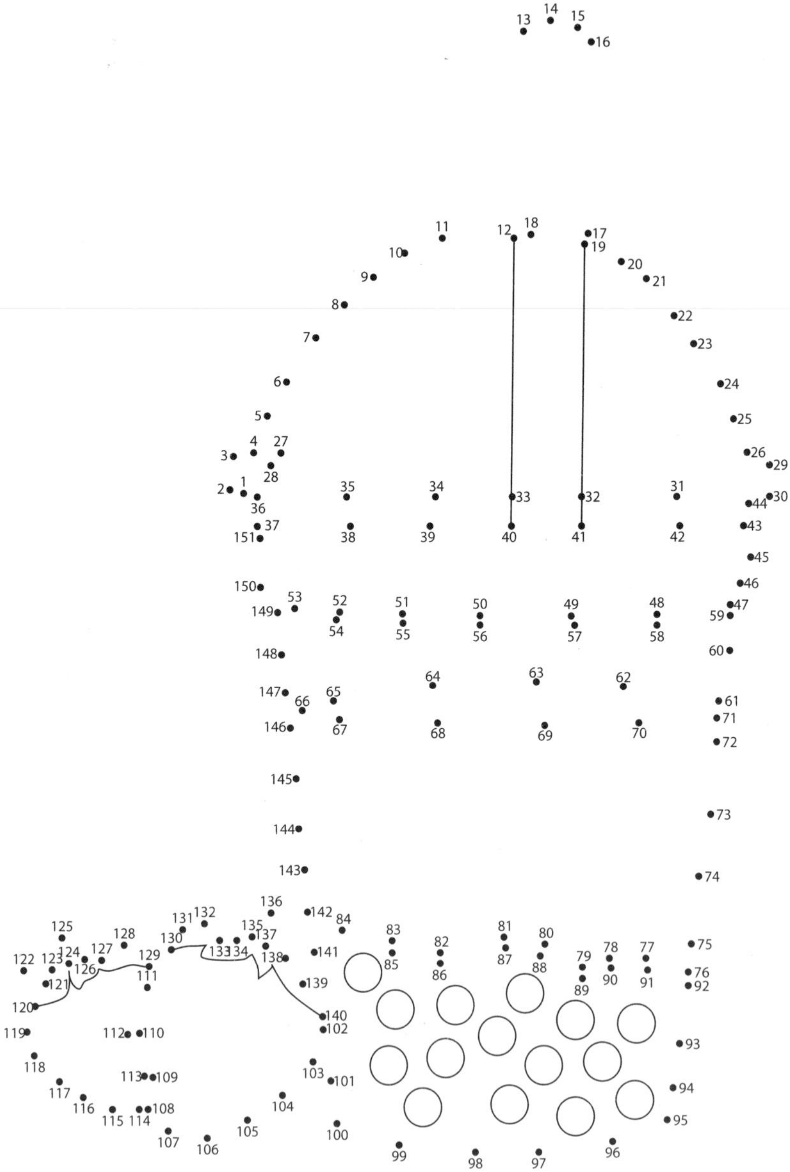

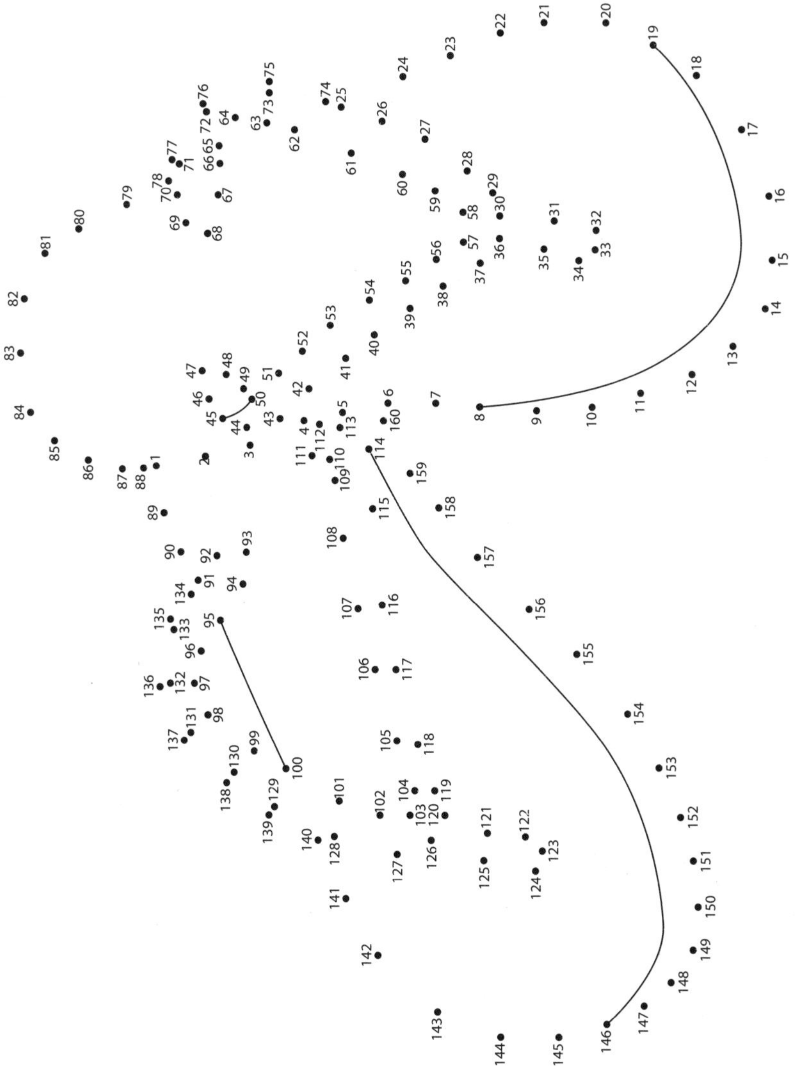

85

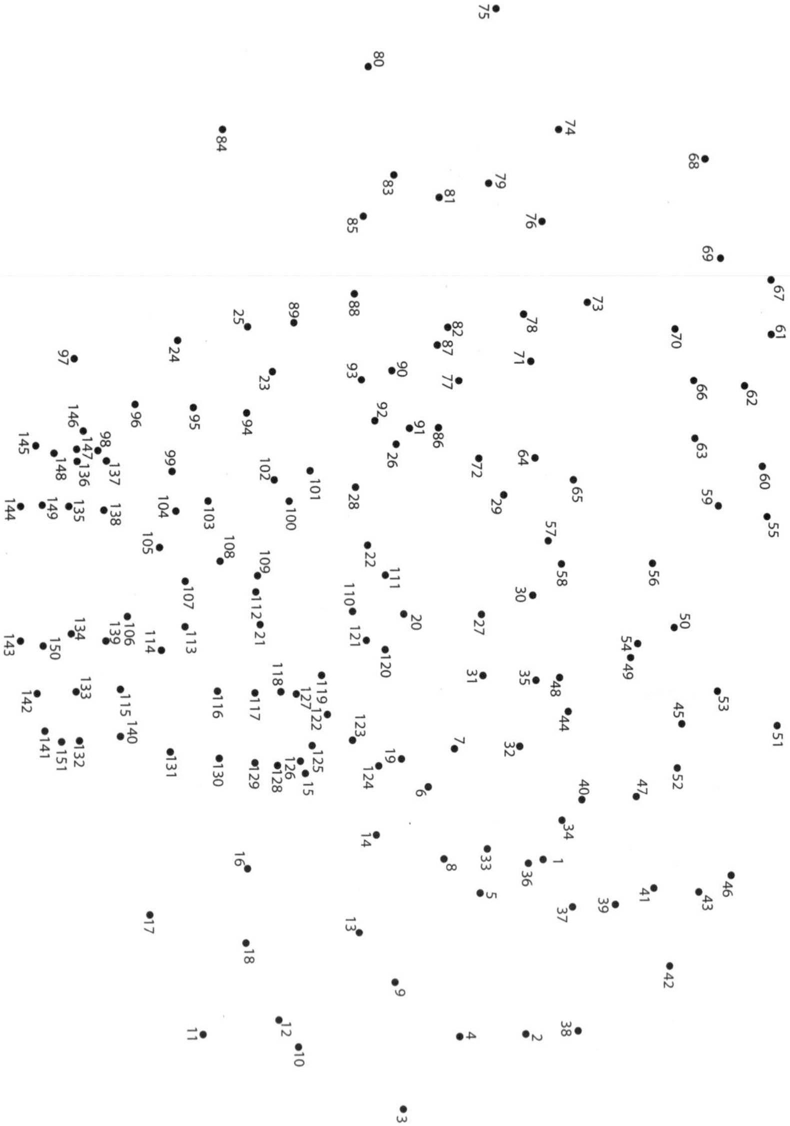

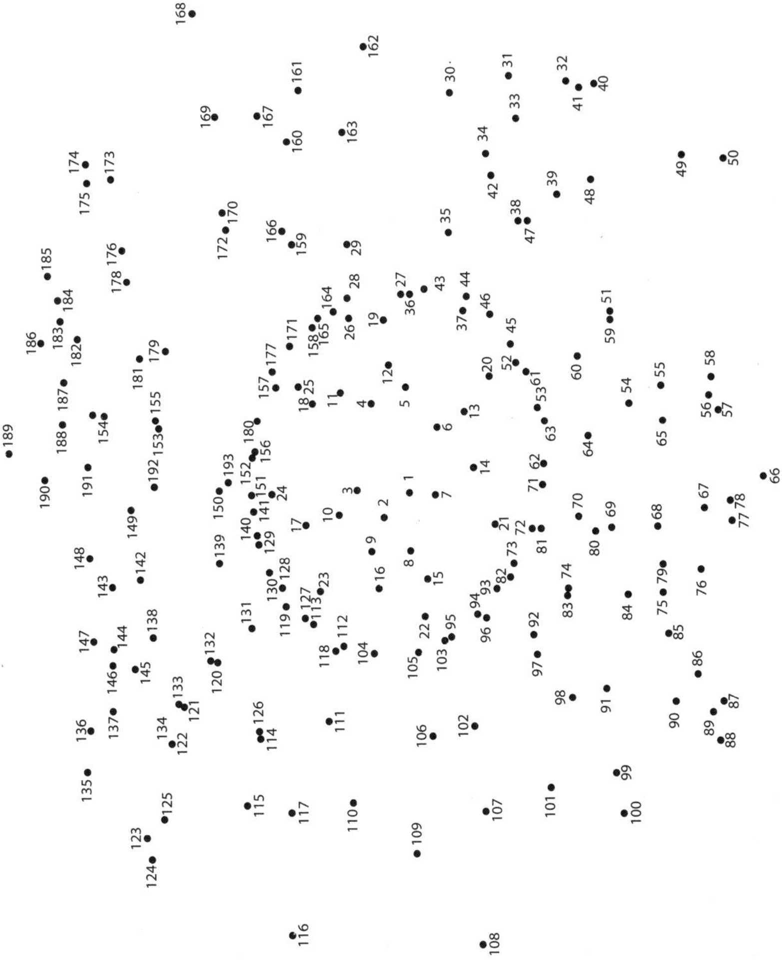

89

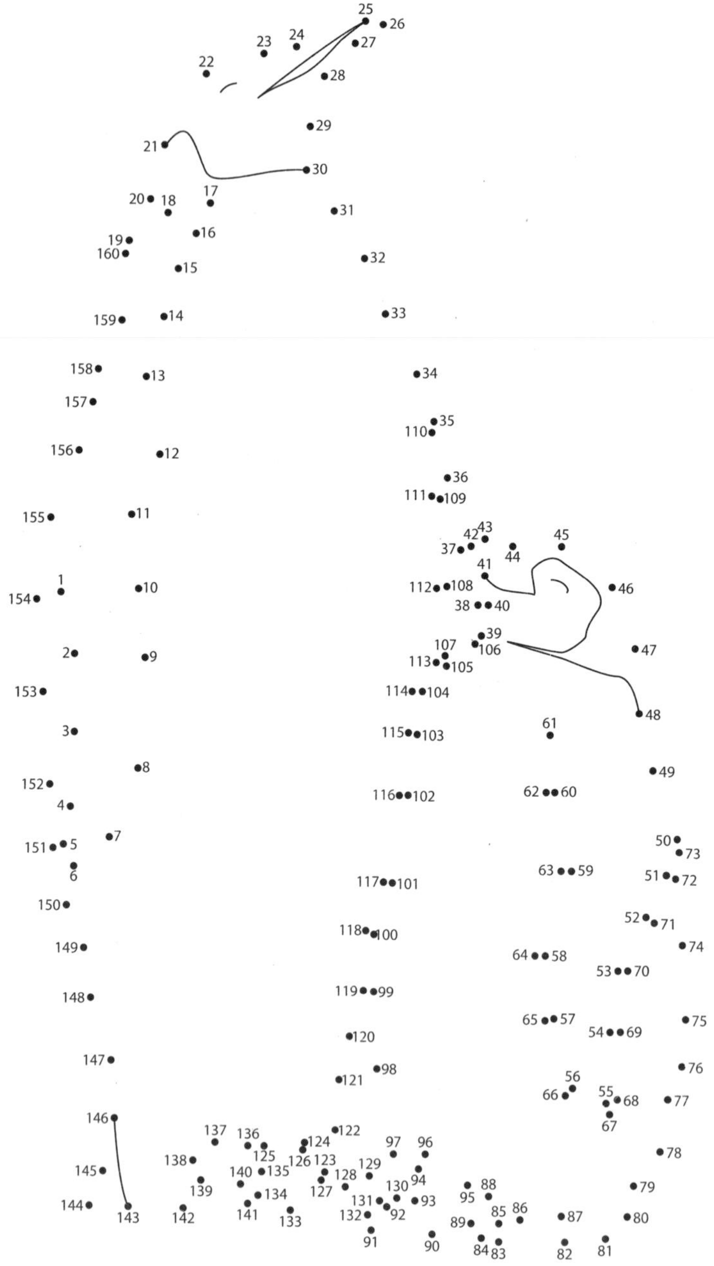

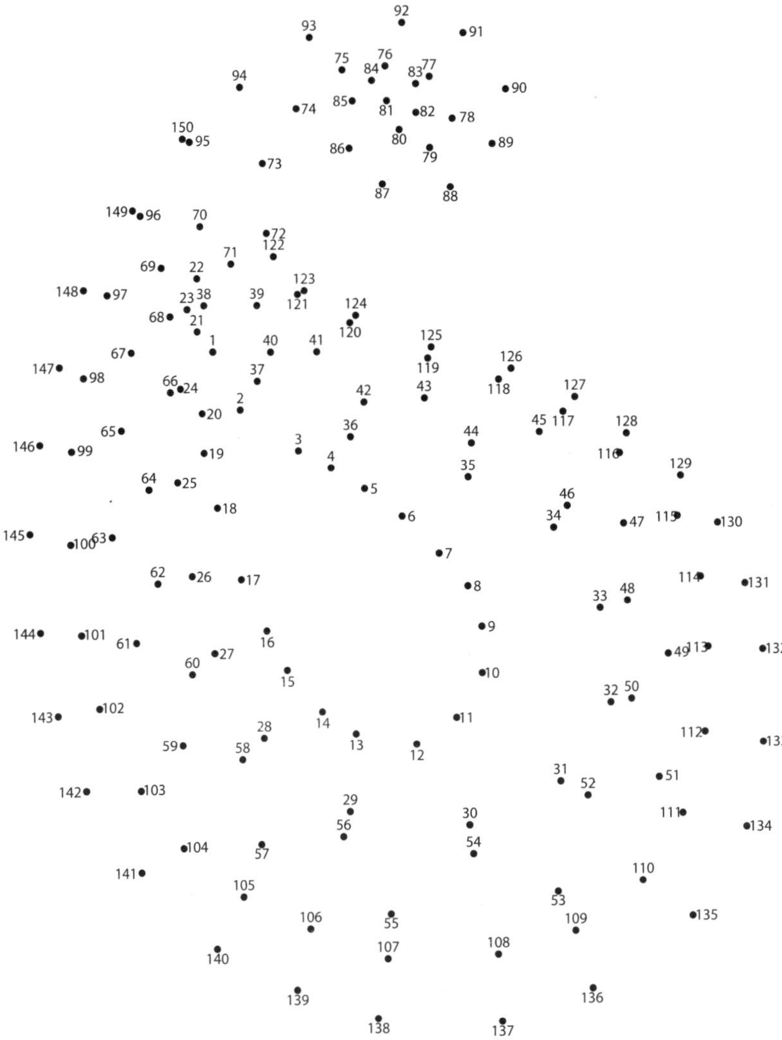

91

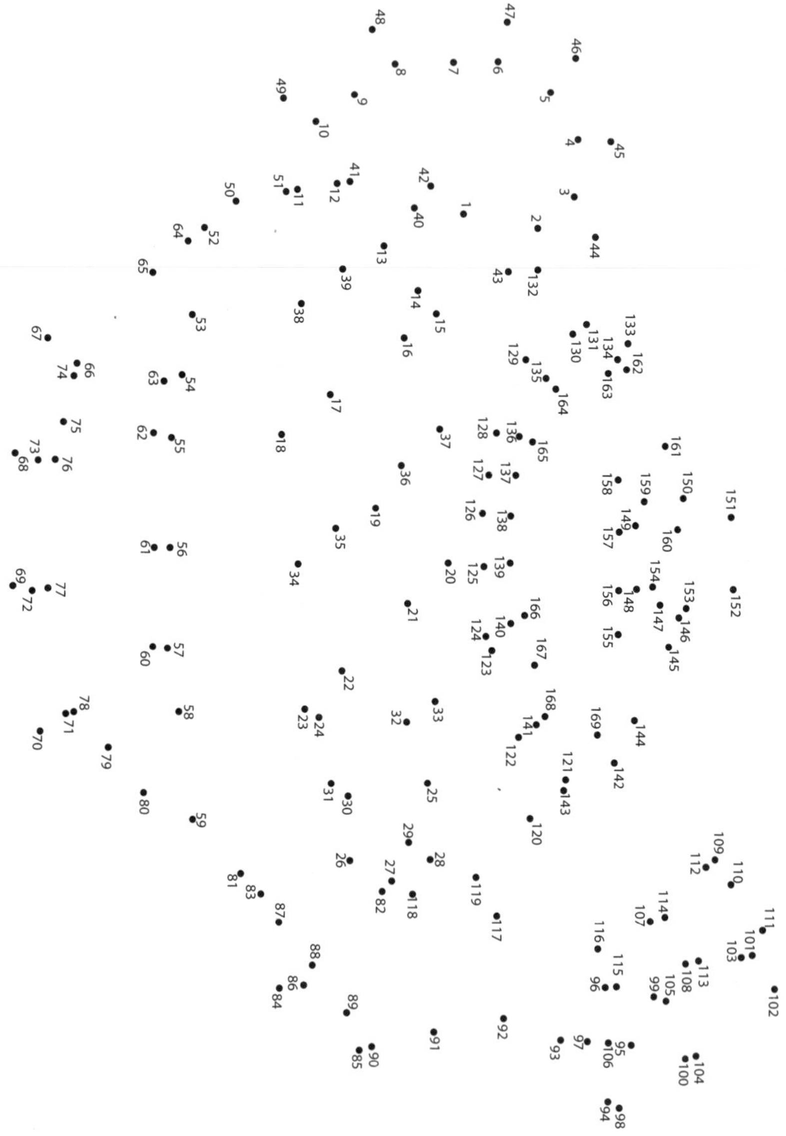

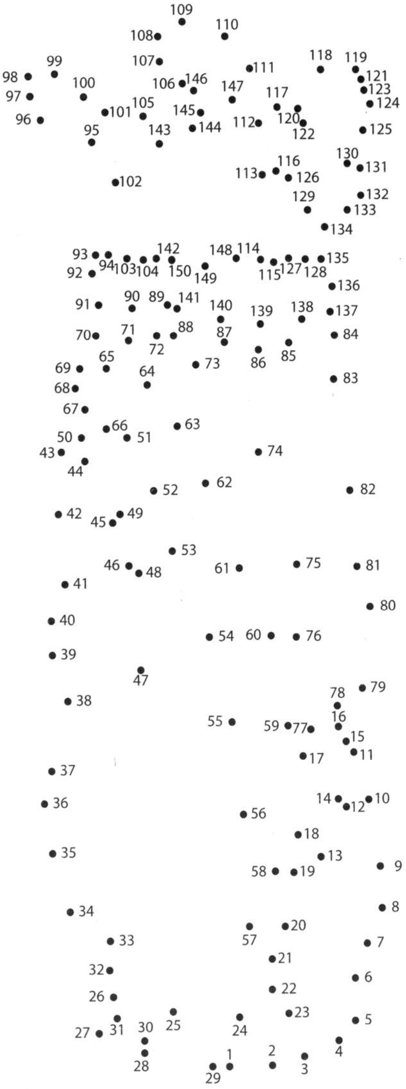

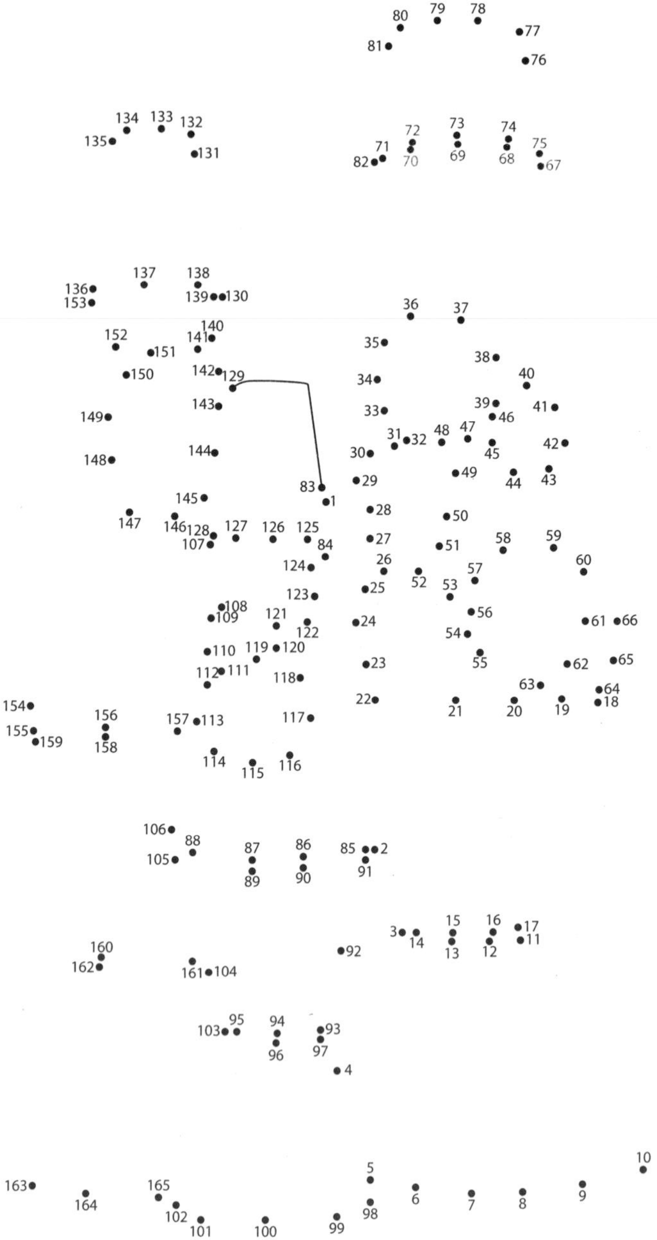

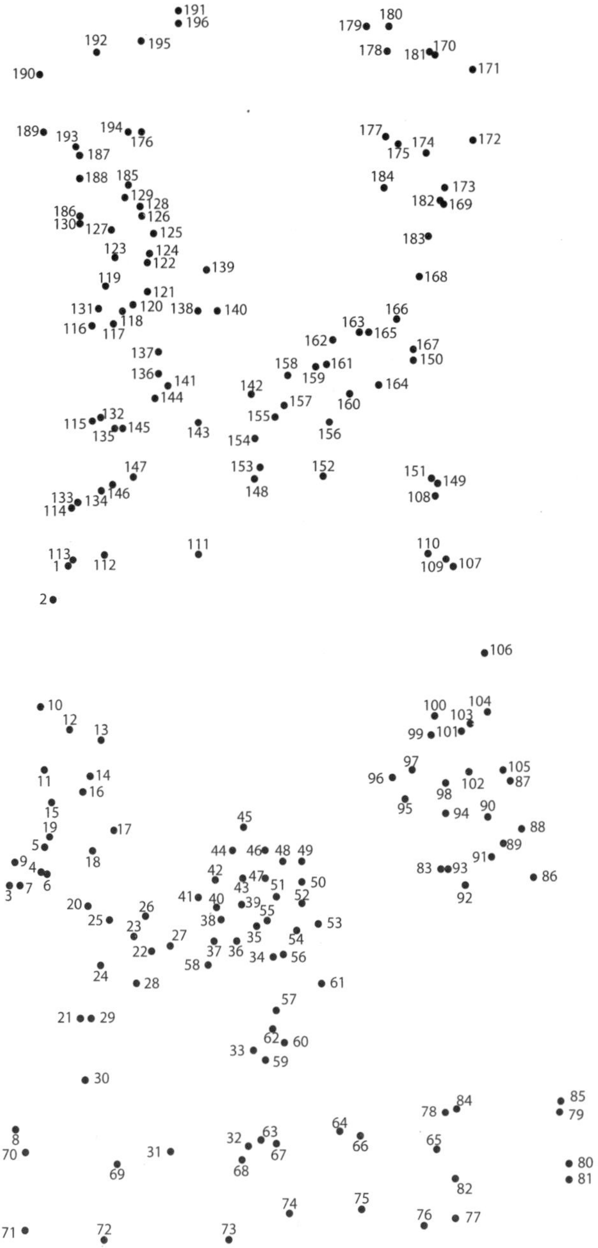

95

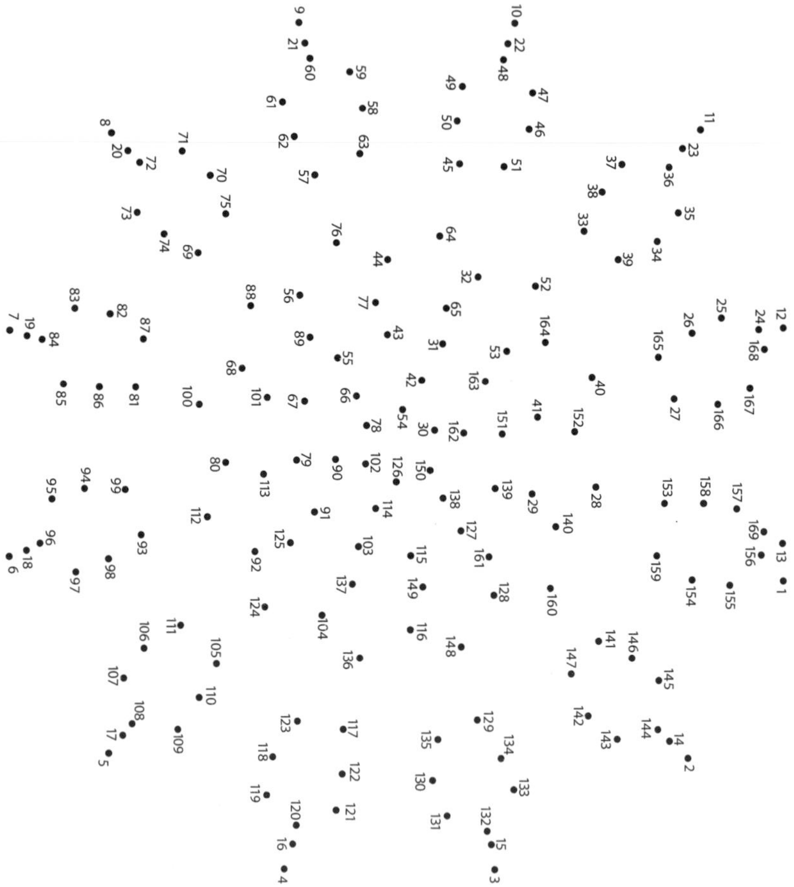

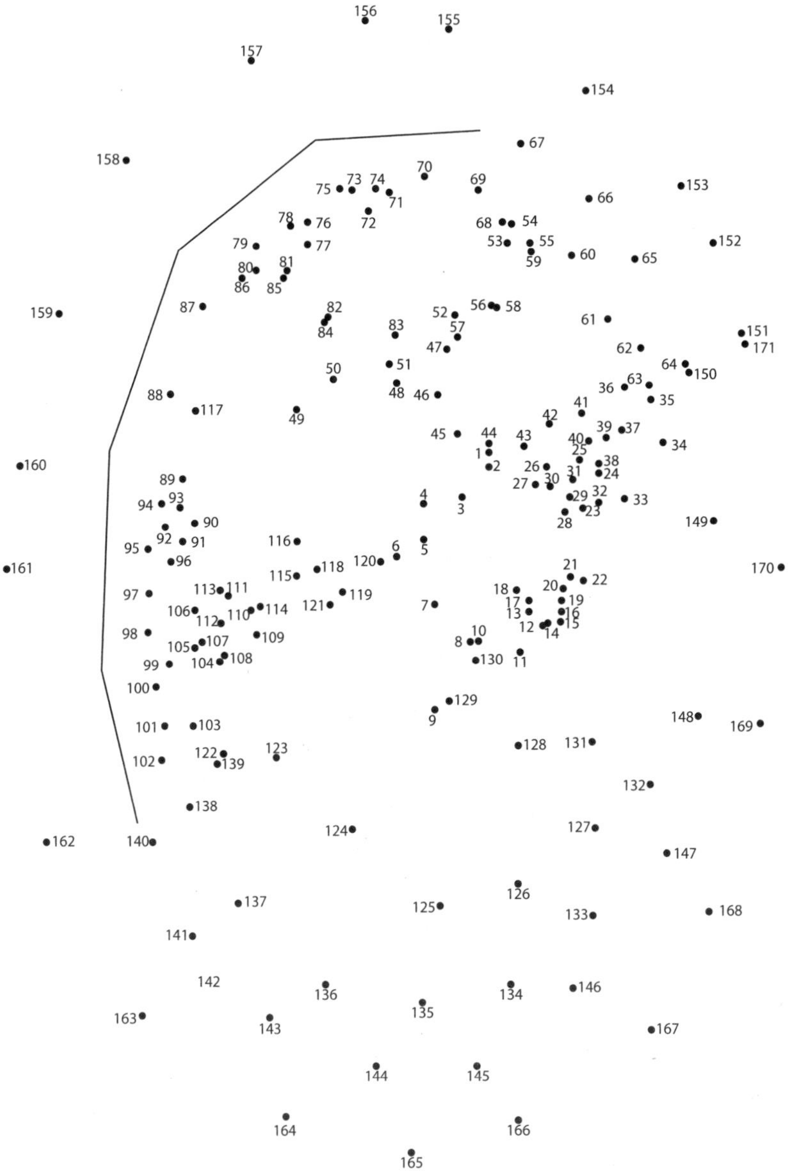

156 155
157
154
158   67
70
75 73 74 69
71   66   153
78   76 72   68 54
79   77   53 55   152
80 81   59 60 65
86 85
87   82   56 58   61   151 171
84   83   62   64
52 57   36 63 150
50 51 47   35
88 117   48 46
49   45 44 43 42 41
1 2   26 40 39 37 34
160   89   4 30 31 25 38
94 93 90   3   27 29 32 24 33
95 92 91   28 23 149
96 116   6 5   21
97   113 111 115 118 120 18 20 22 170
98 106 112 110 114 119 17 19
105 107 109   7 13 16
99 104 108   10 12 14 15
100   8 130 11
129
101 103   9
102 122 123   128 131 148 169
139
138   132
140   124   127 147
162
137 125 126 133 168
141
142 136 134 146
163 143   135 167
144 145
164 166
165

97

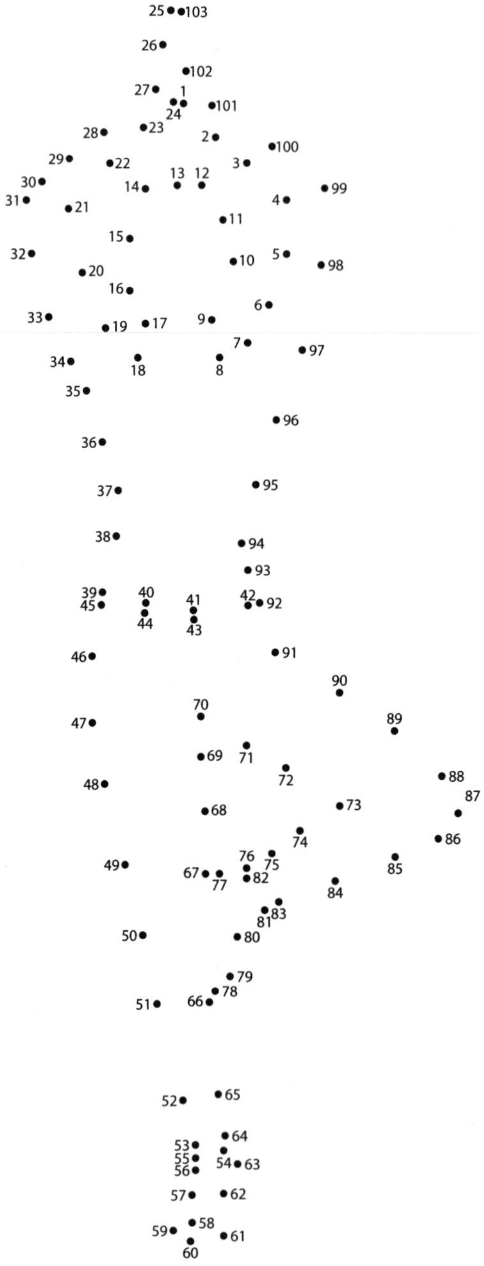

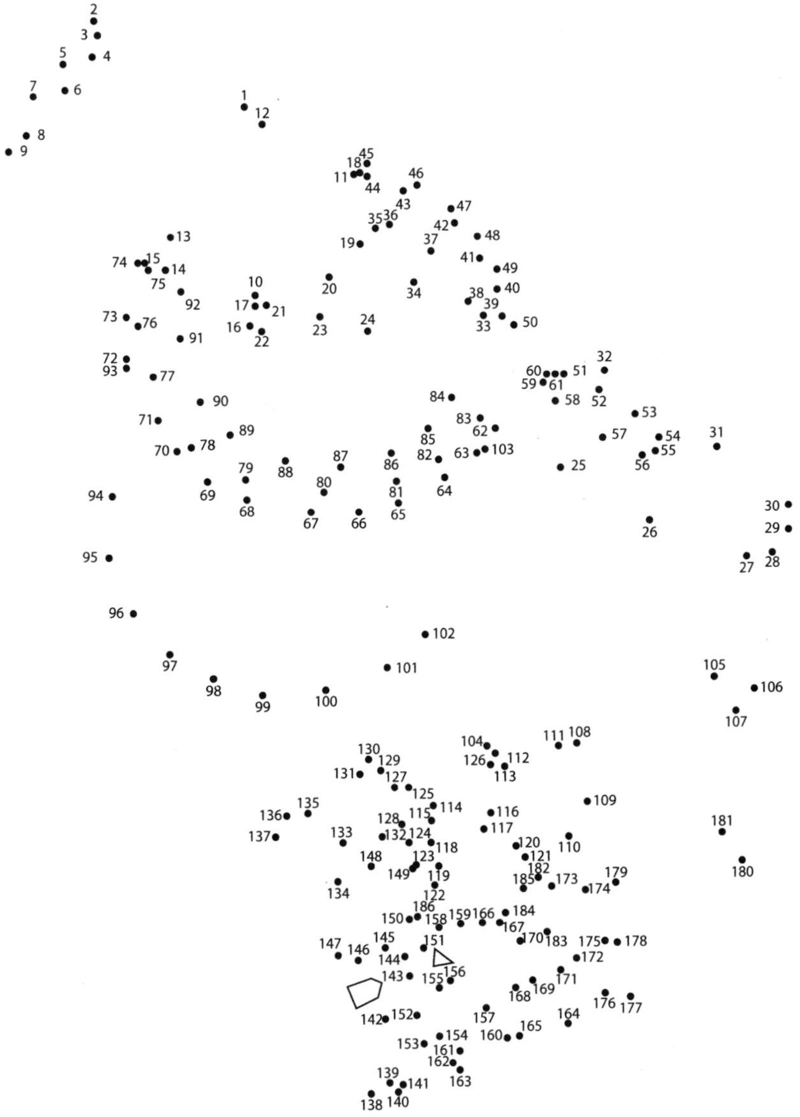

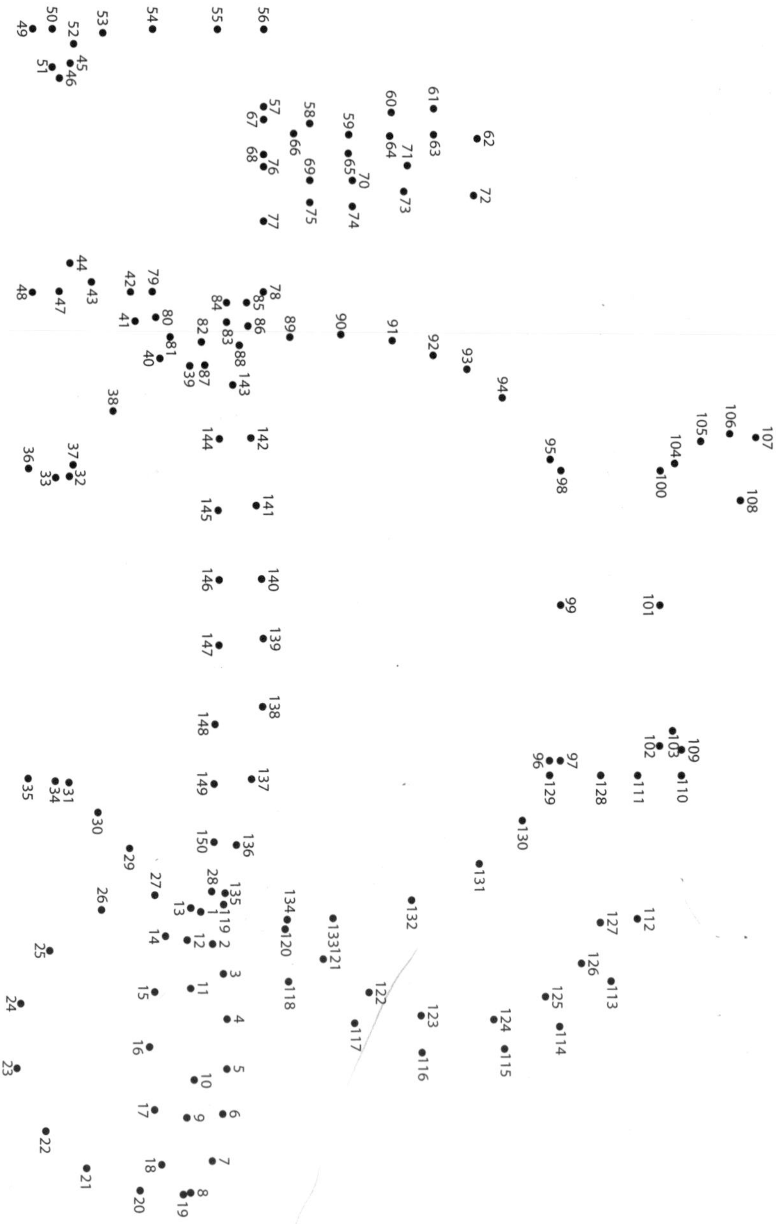

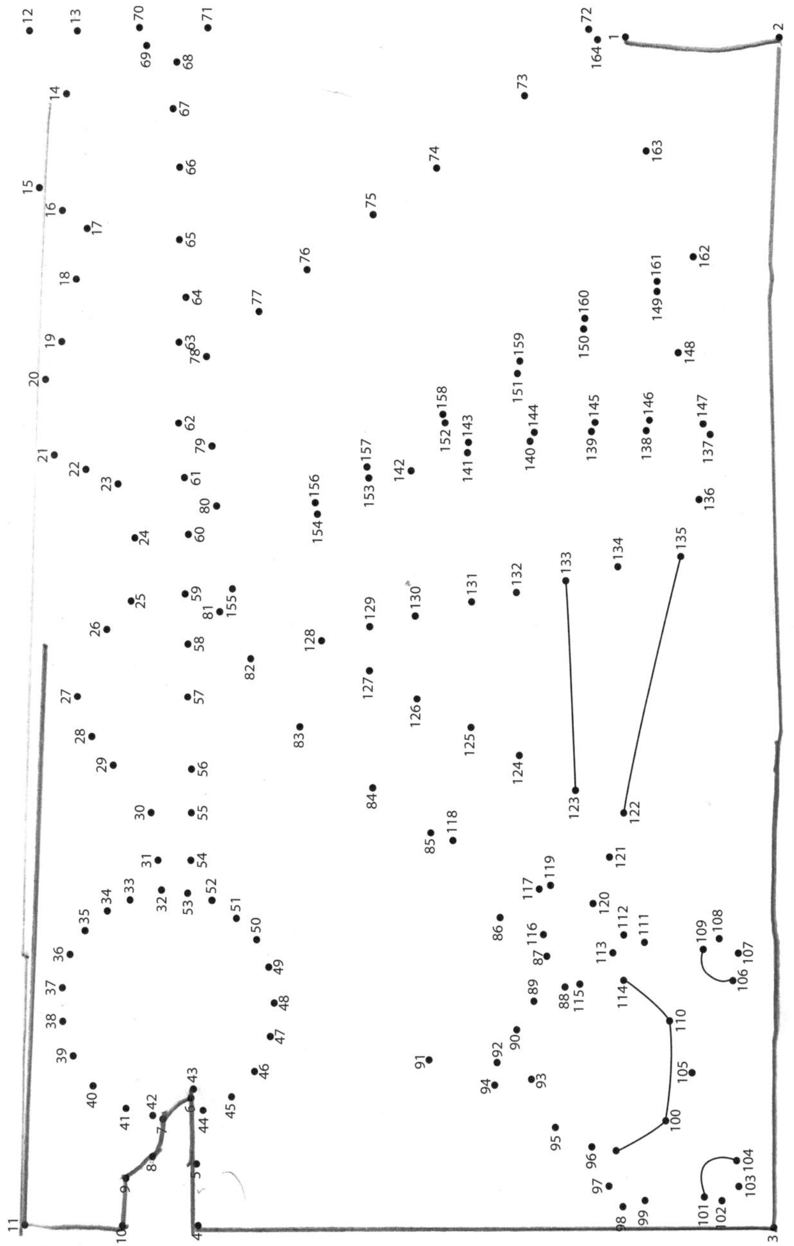

101

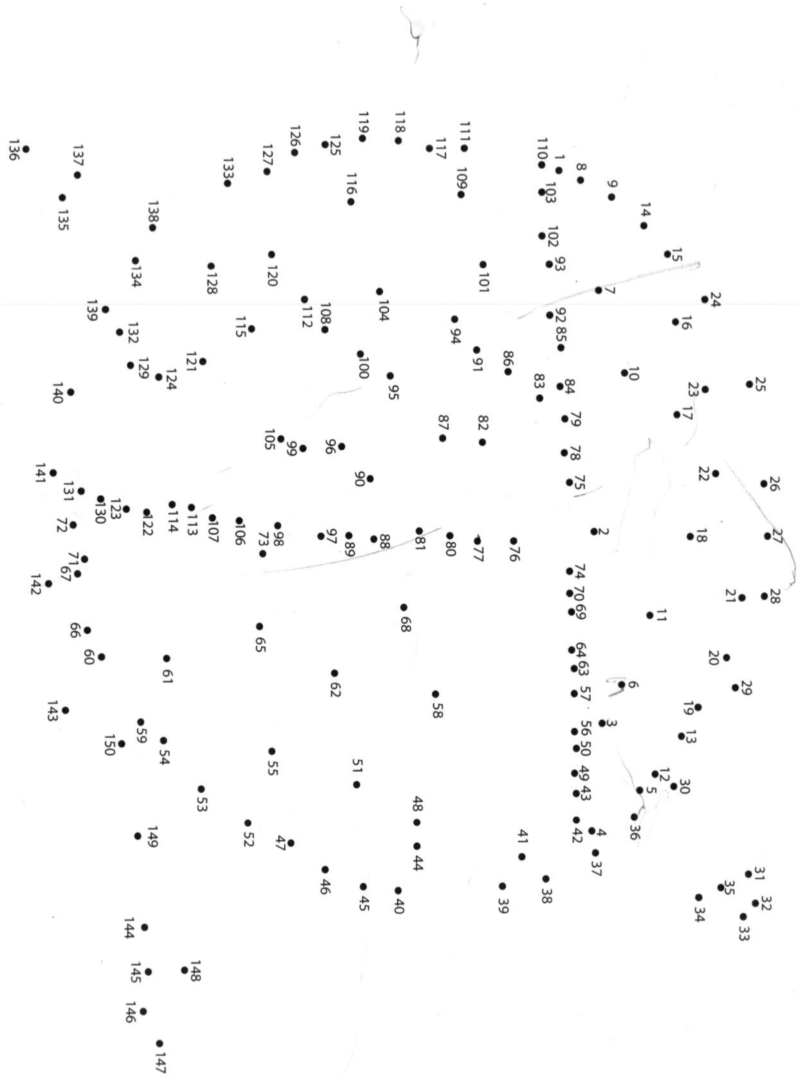

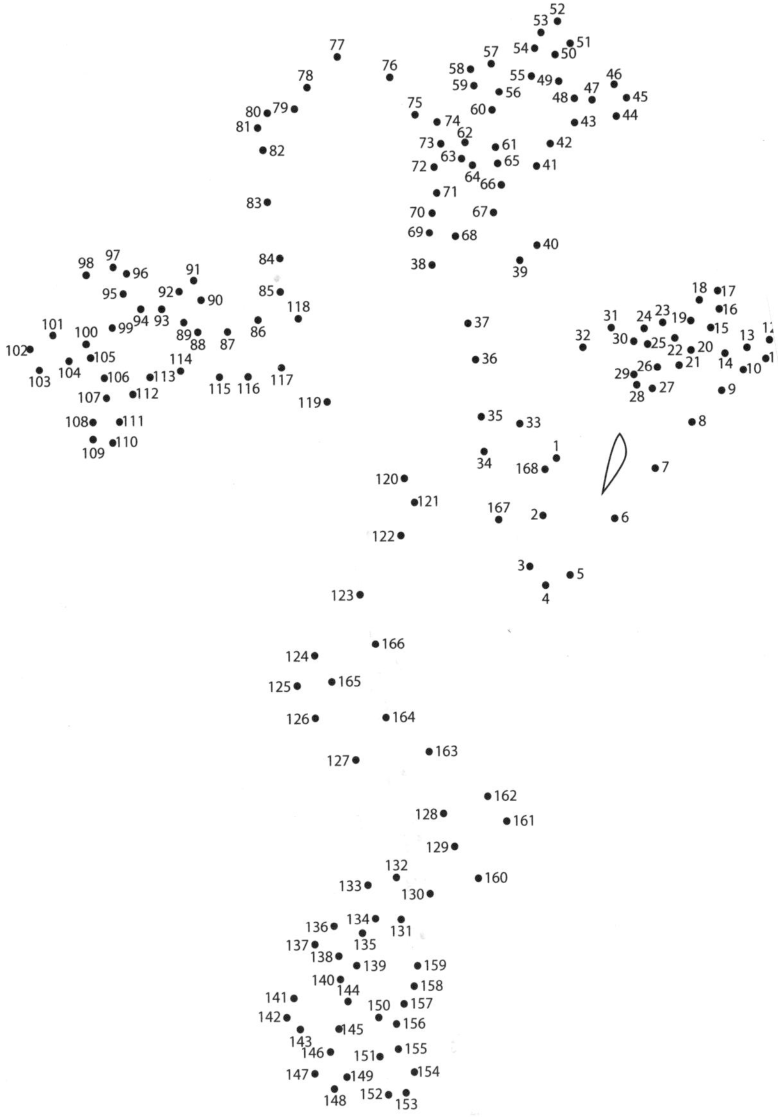
1
2
3
4
5
6
7
8
9
10
11
12
13
14
15
16
17
18
19
20
21
22
23
24
25
26
27
28
29
30
31
32
33
34
35
36
37
38
39
40
41
42
43
44
45
46
47
48
49
50
51
52
53
54
55
56
57
58
59
60
61
62
63
64
65
66
67
68
69
70
71
72
73
74
75
76
77
78
79
80
81
82
83
84
85
86
87
88
89
90
91
92
93
94
95
96
97
98
99
100
101
102
103
104
105
106
107
108
109
110
111
112
113
114
115
116
117
118
119
120
121
122
123
124
125
126
127
128
129
130
131
132
133
134
135
136
137
138
139
140
141
142
143
144
145
146
147
148
149
150
151
152
153
154
155
156
157
158
159
160
161
162
163
164
165
166
167
168

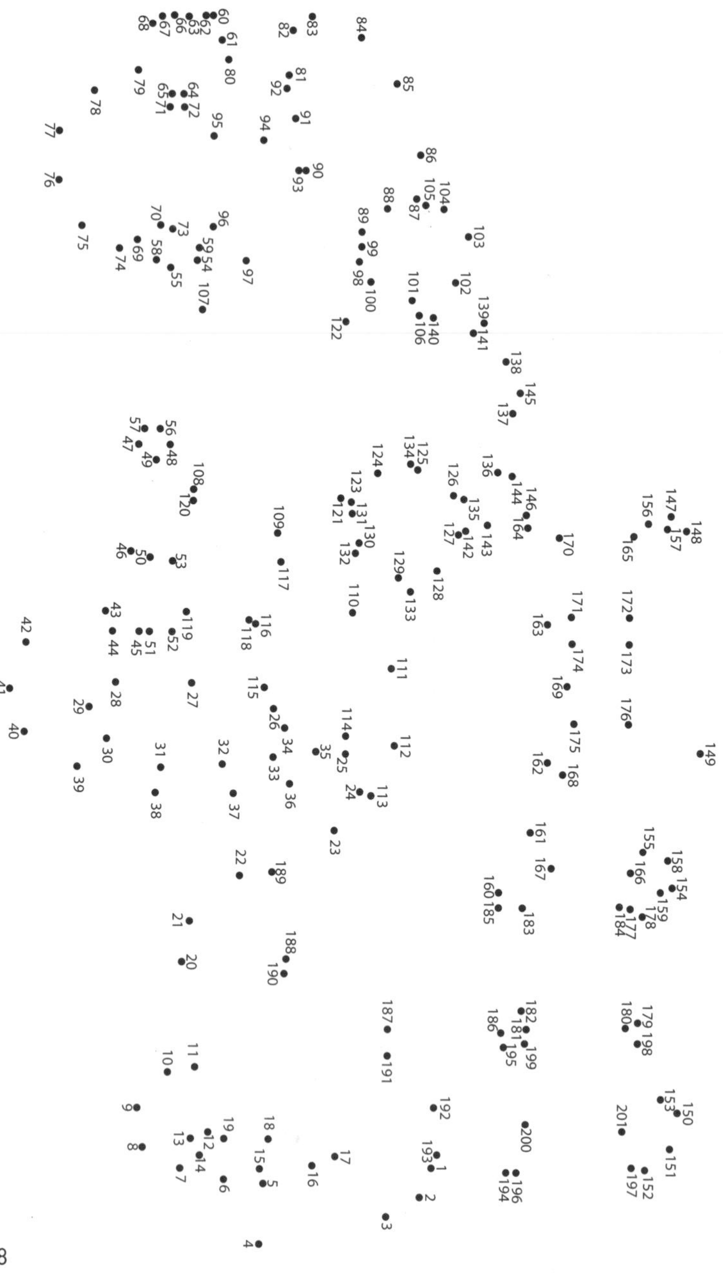

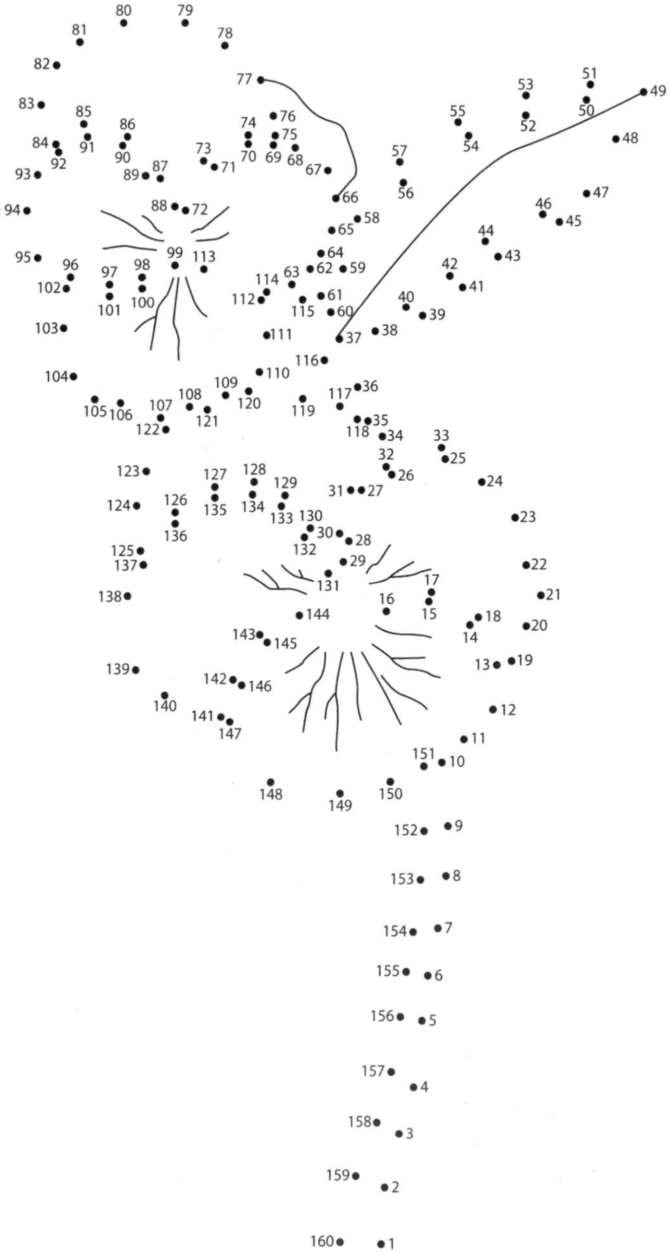

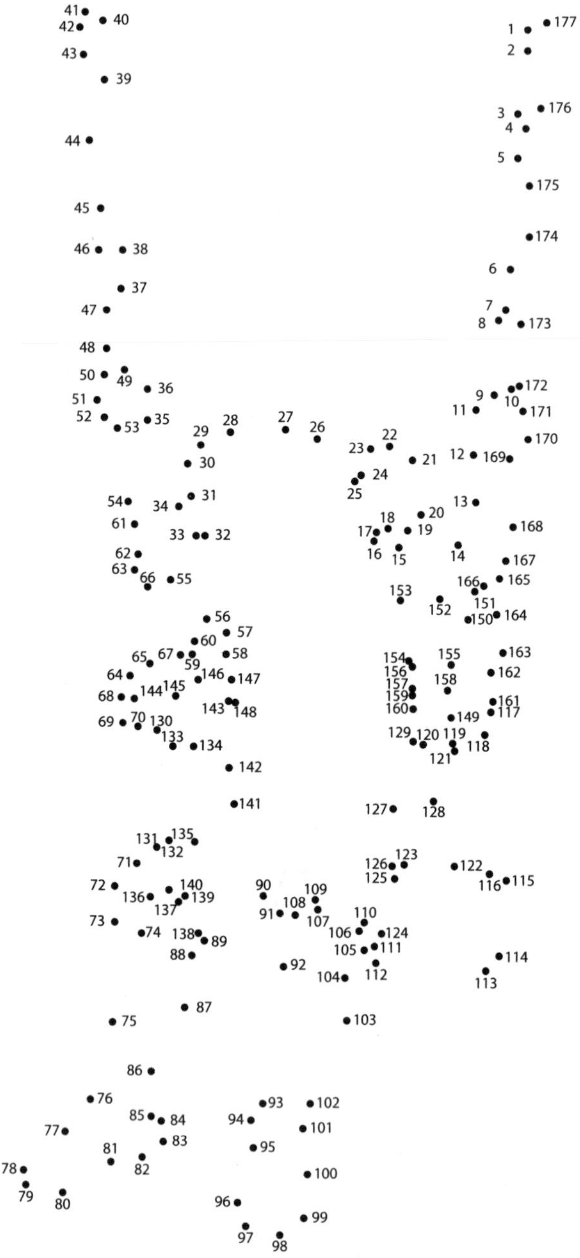

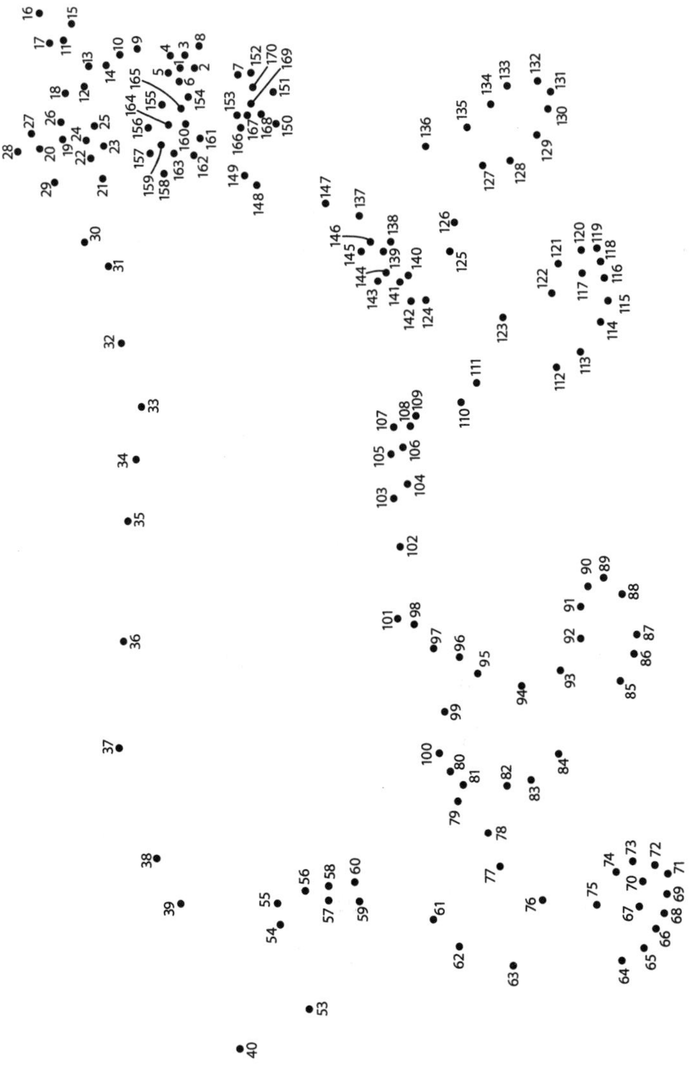

111

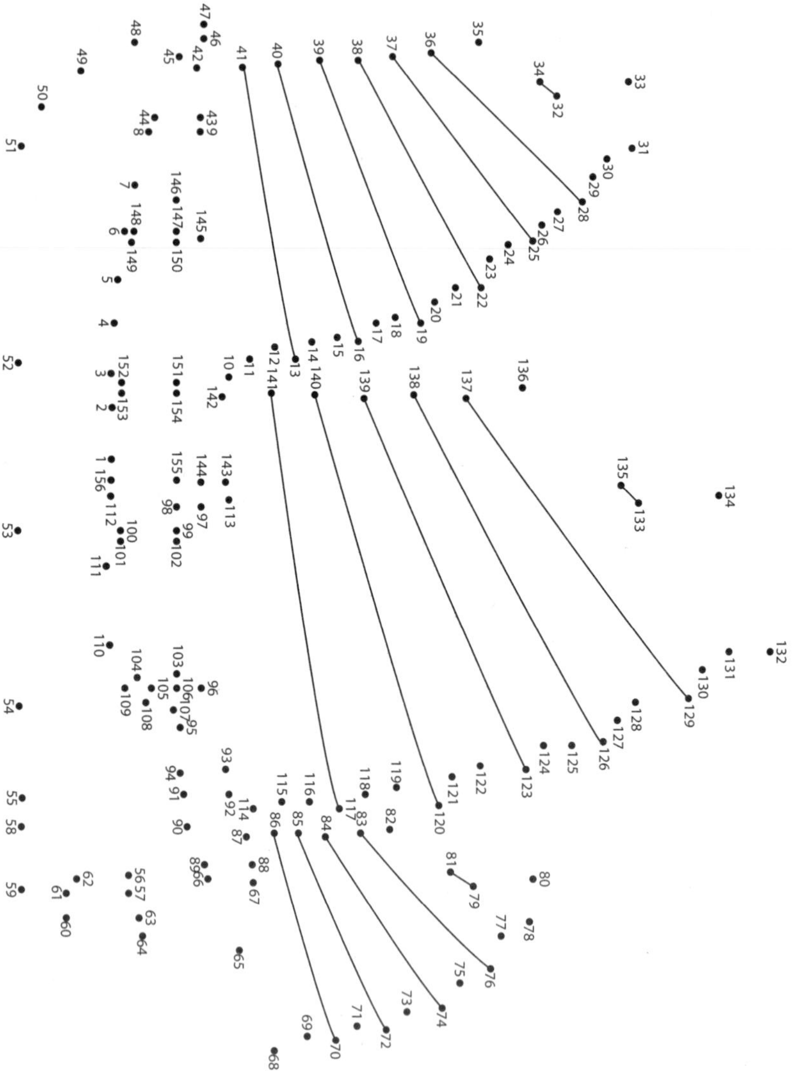

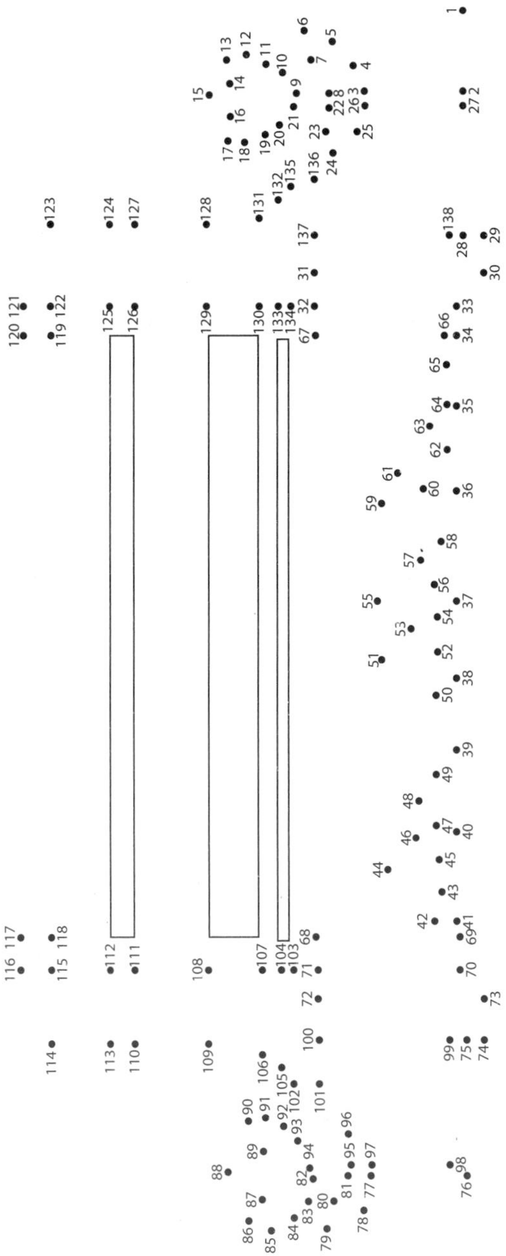

113

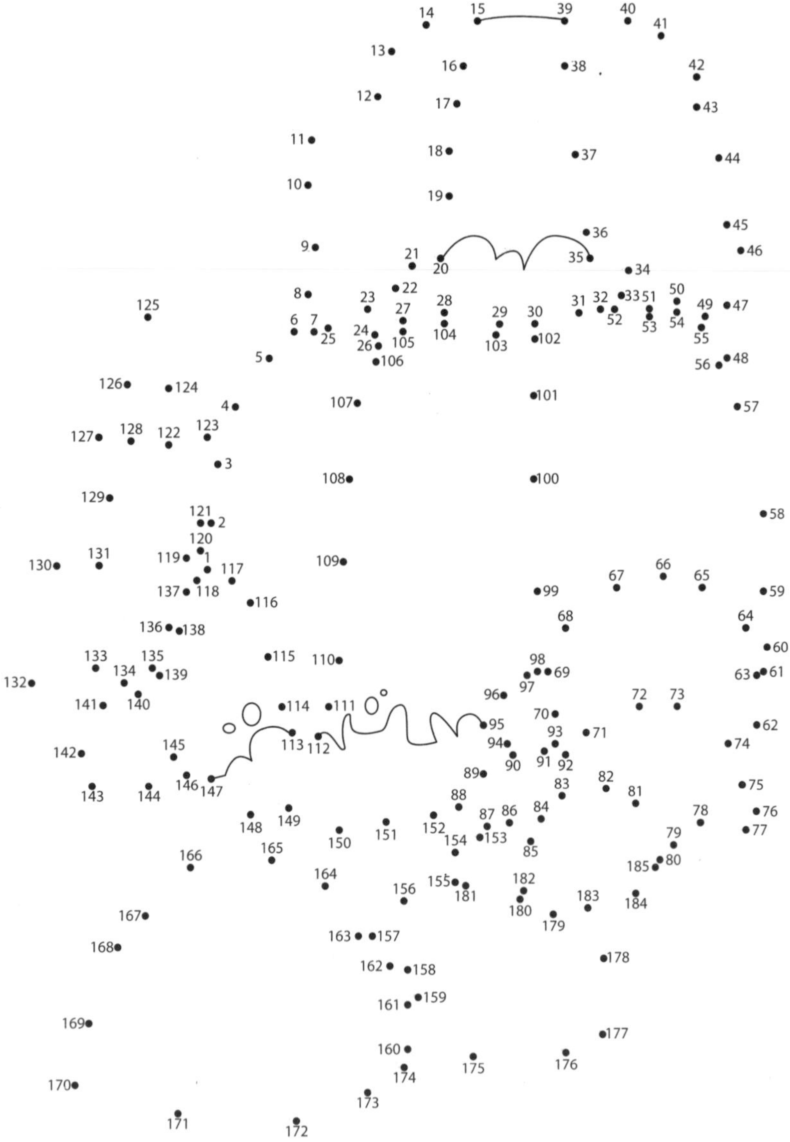

114

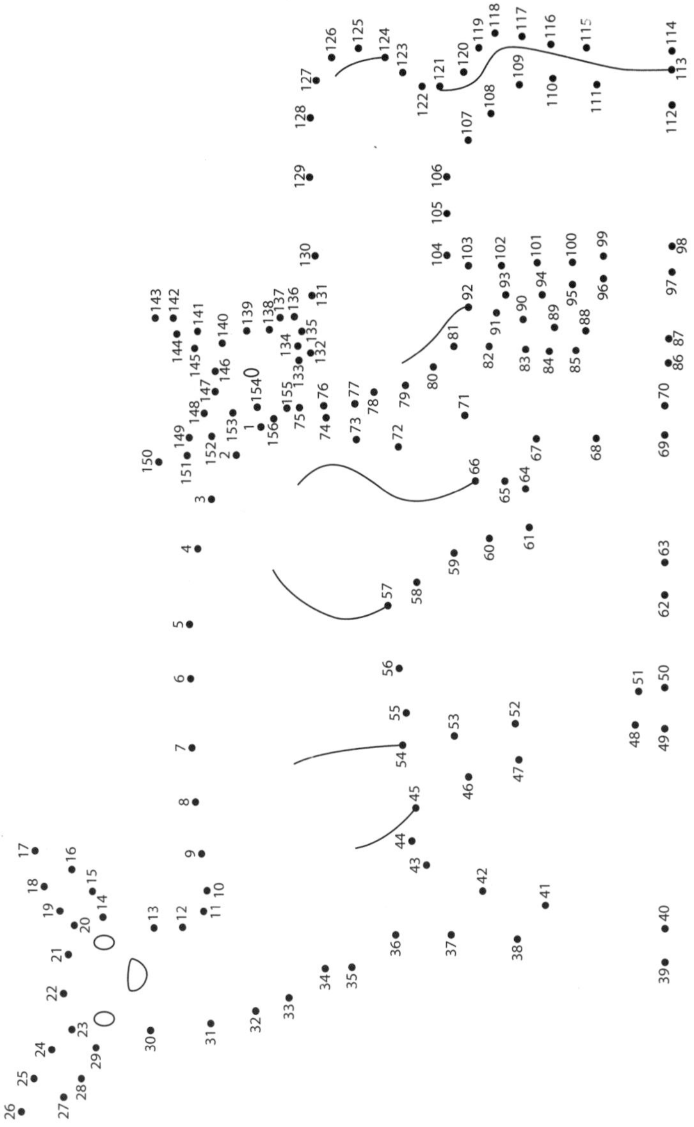

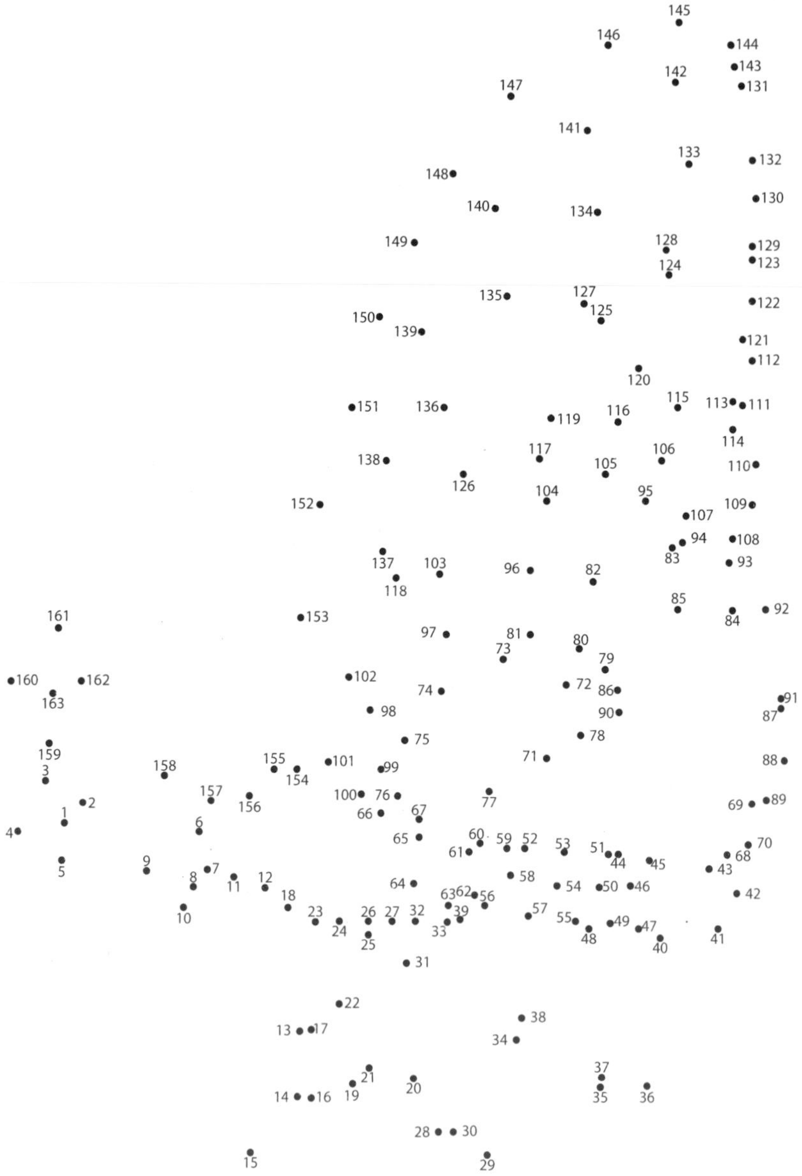

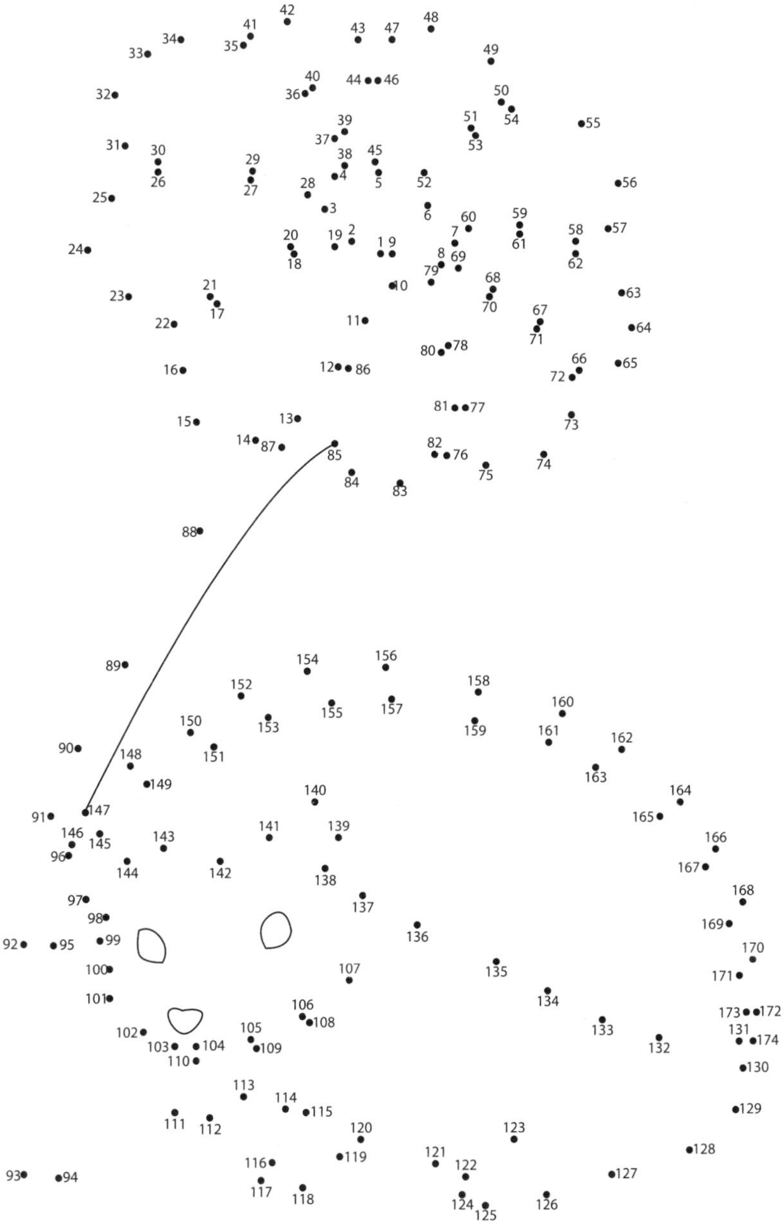

117

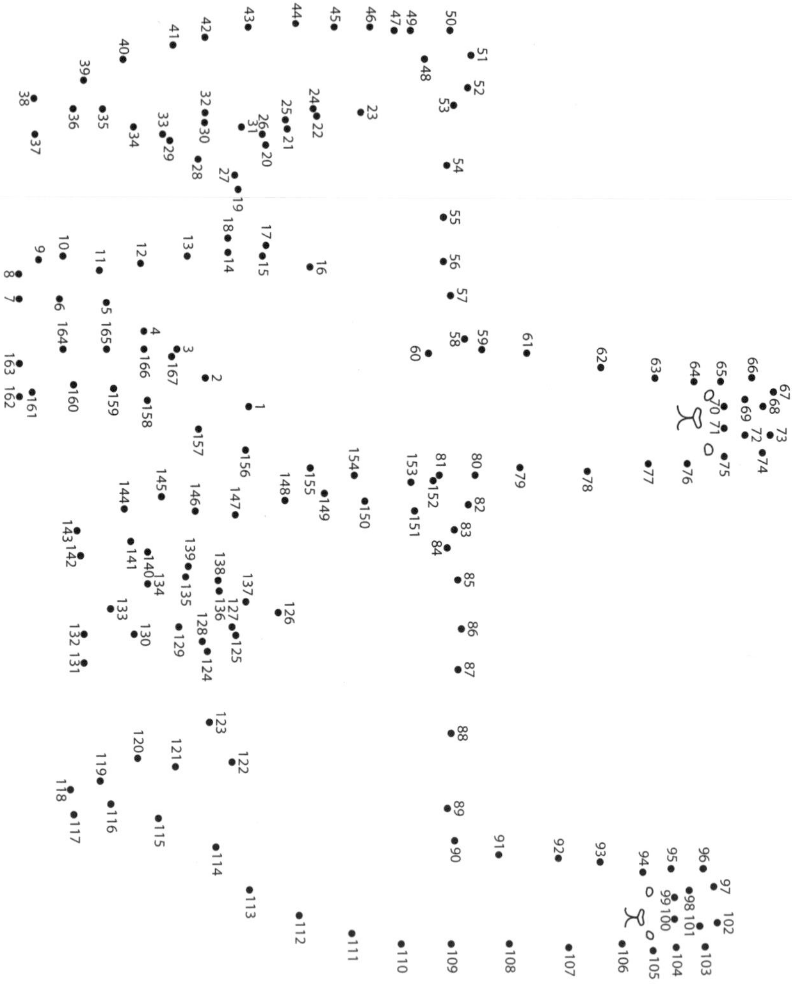

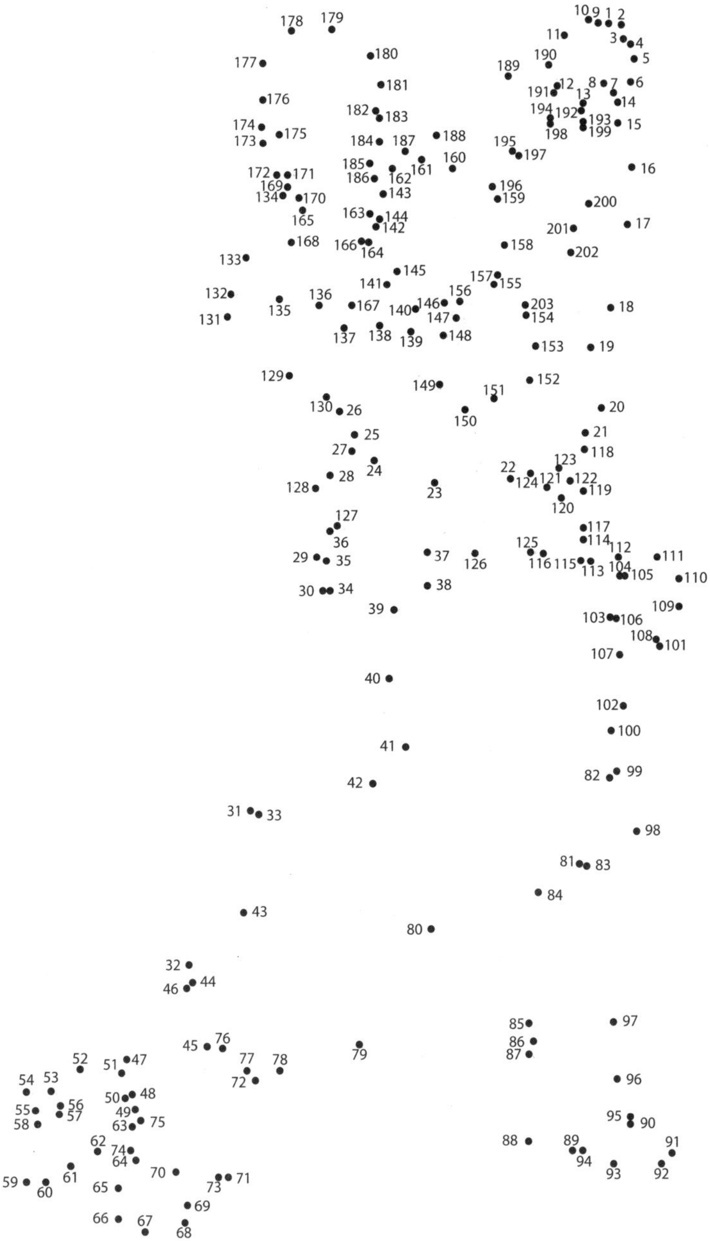

119

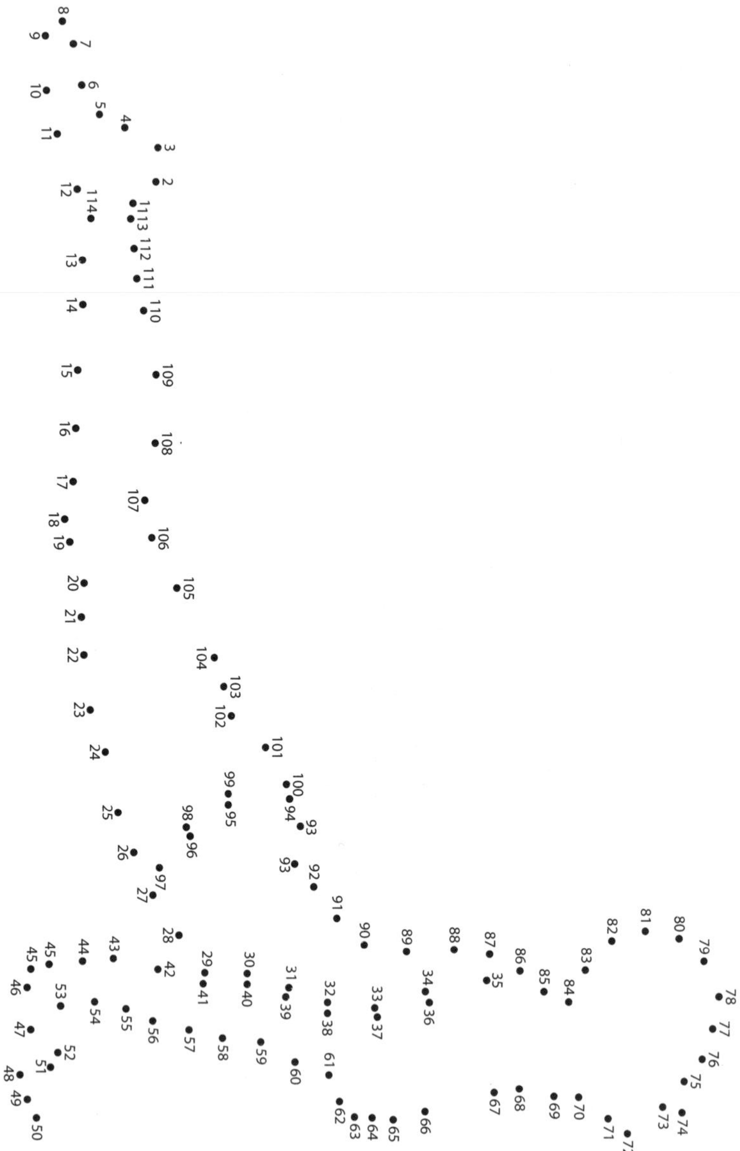

120

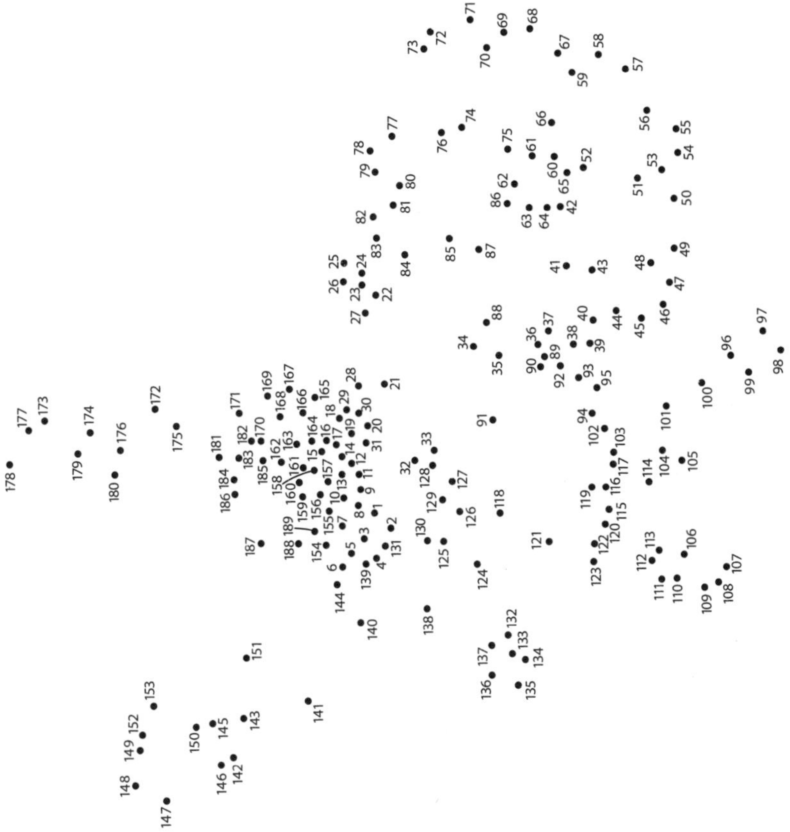

121

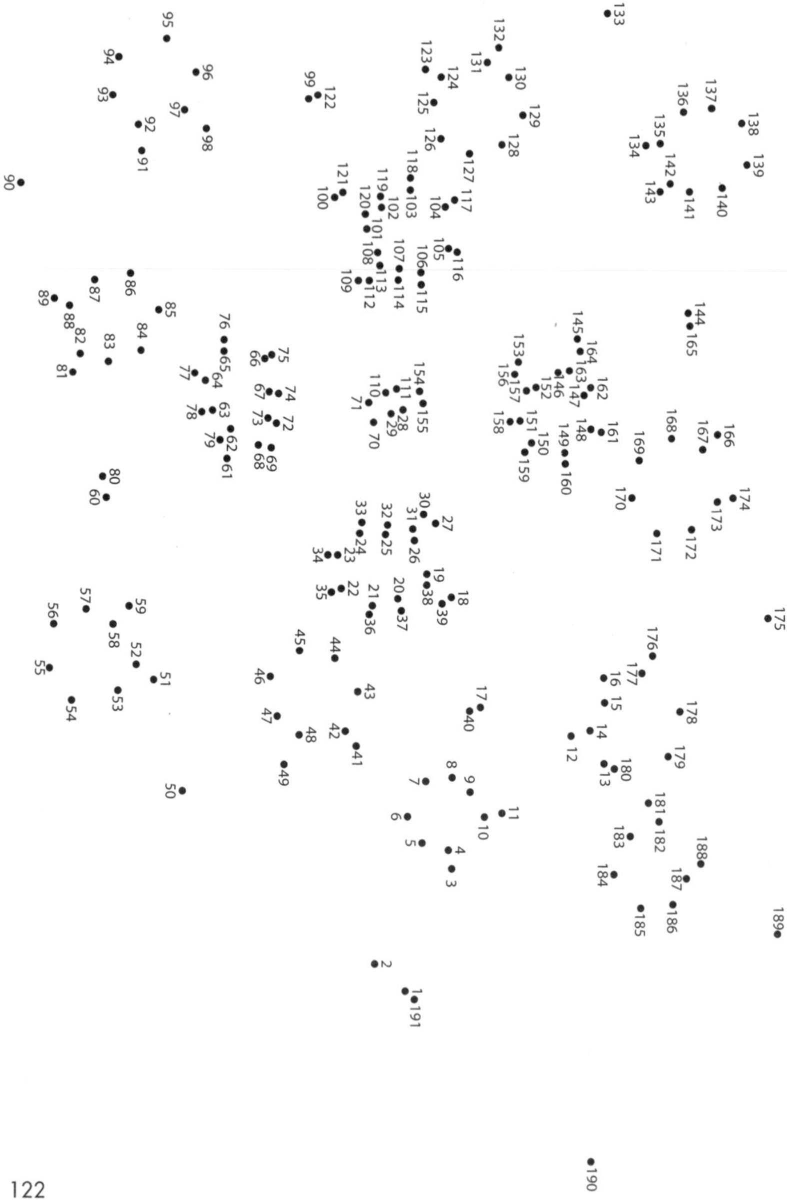

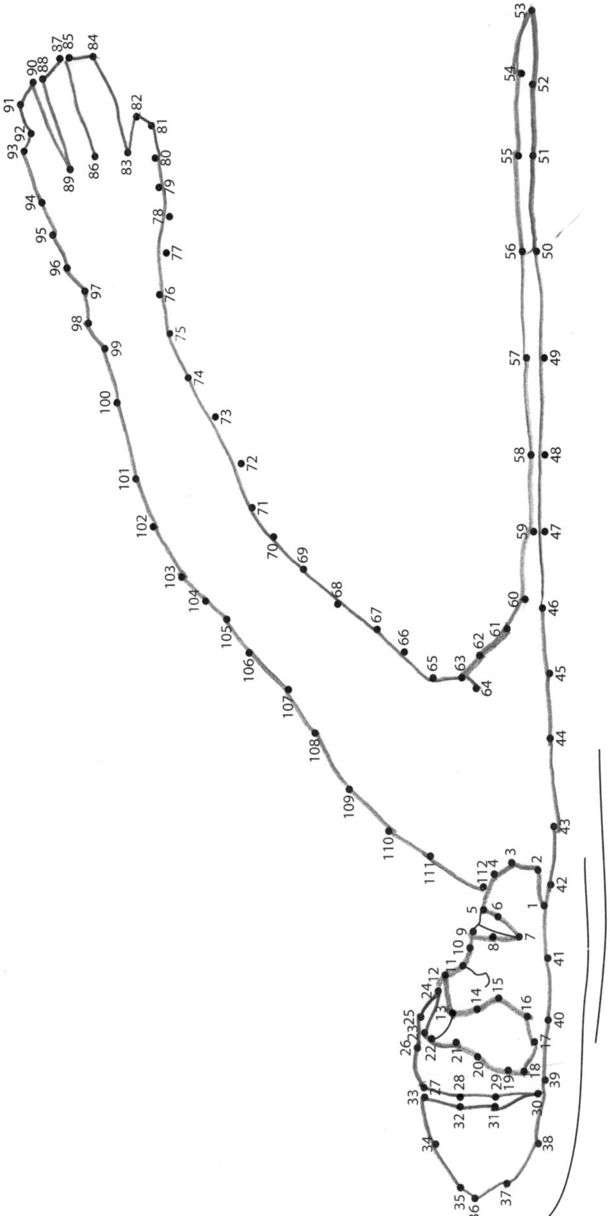

123

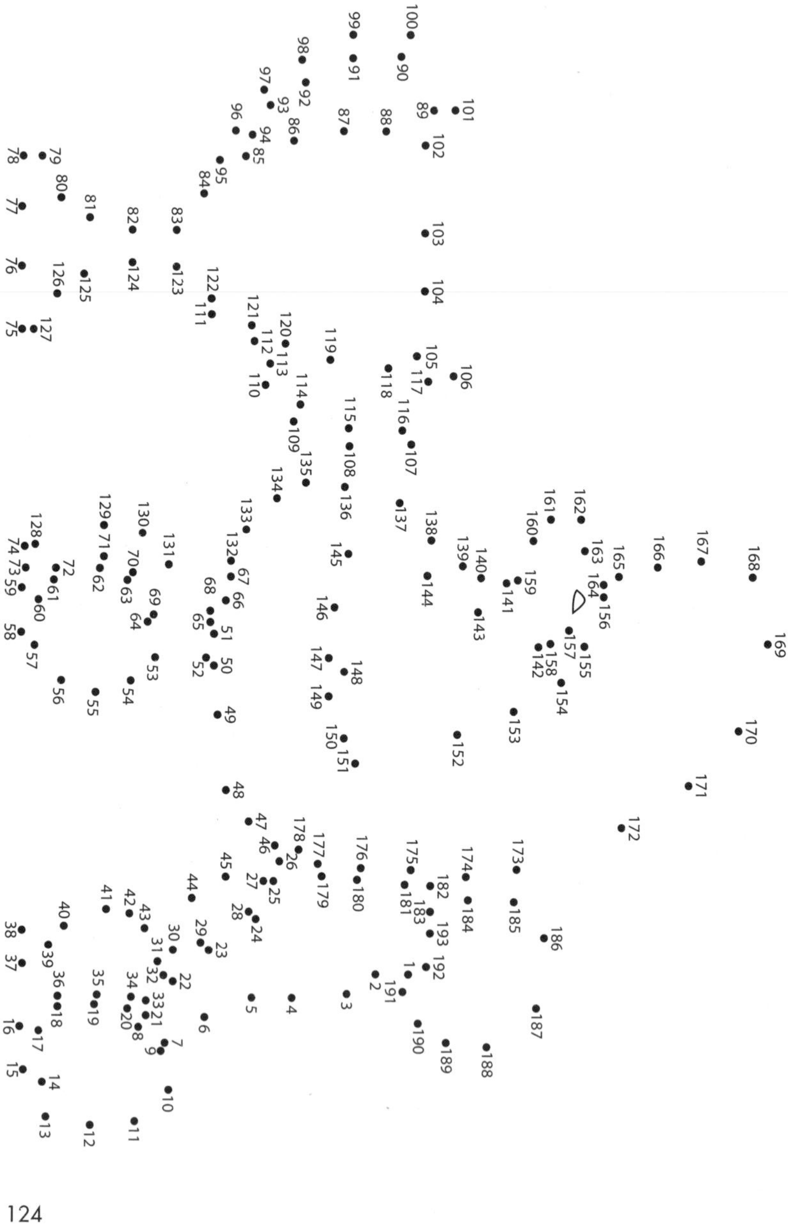

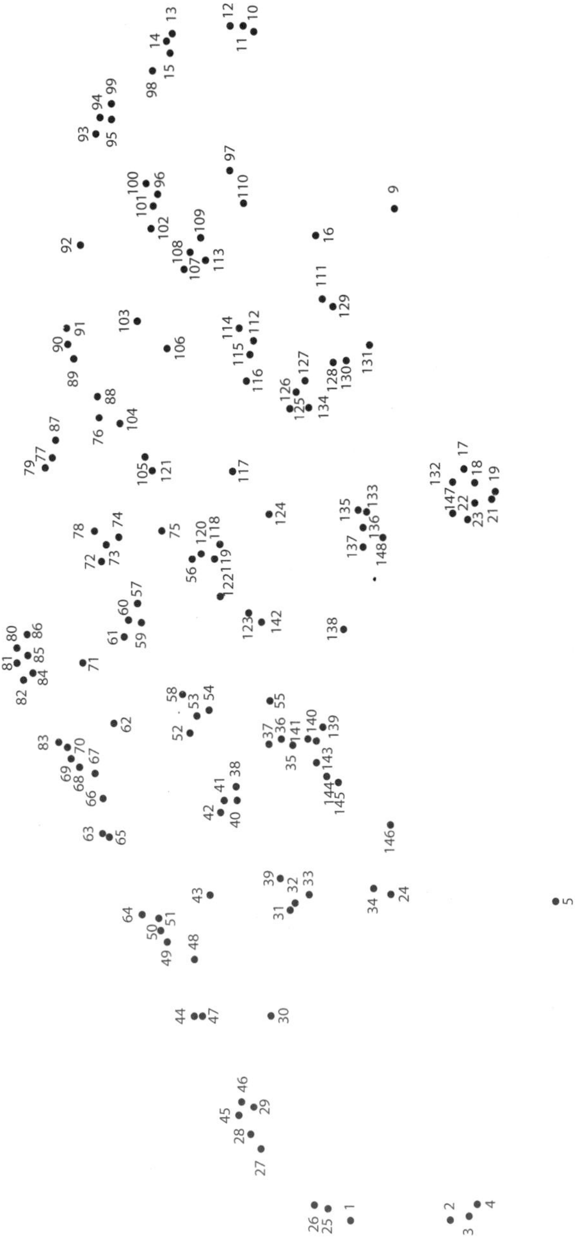

125

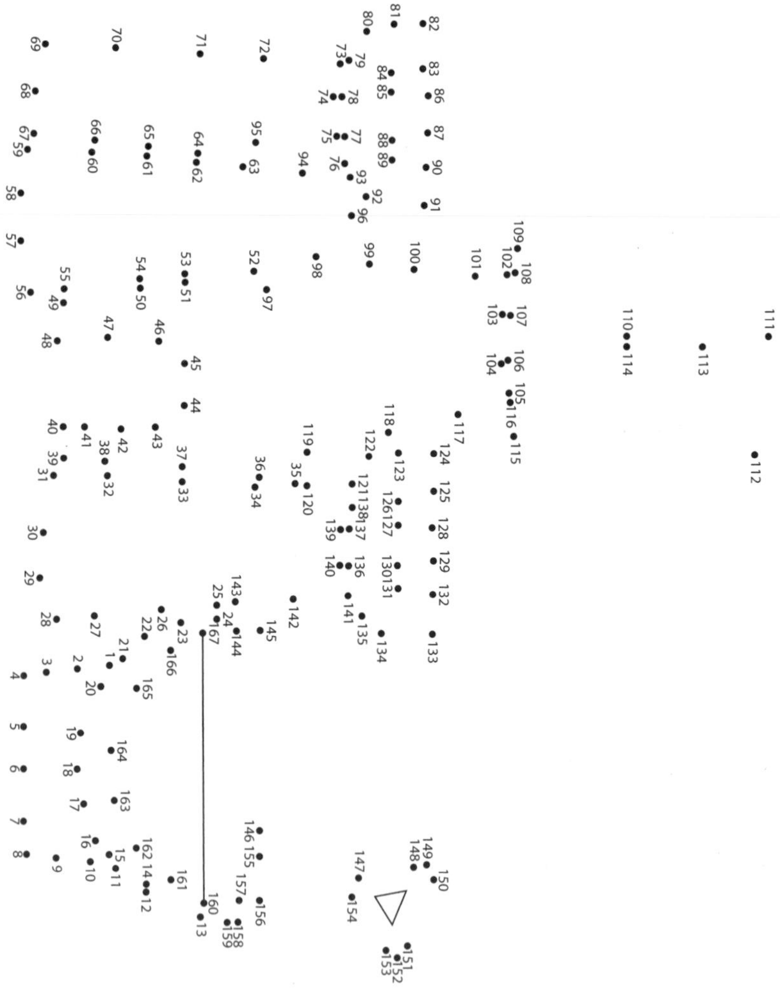

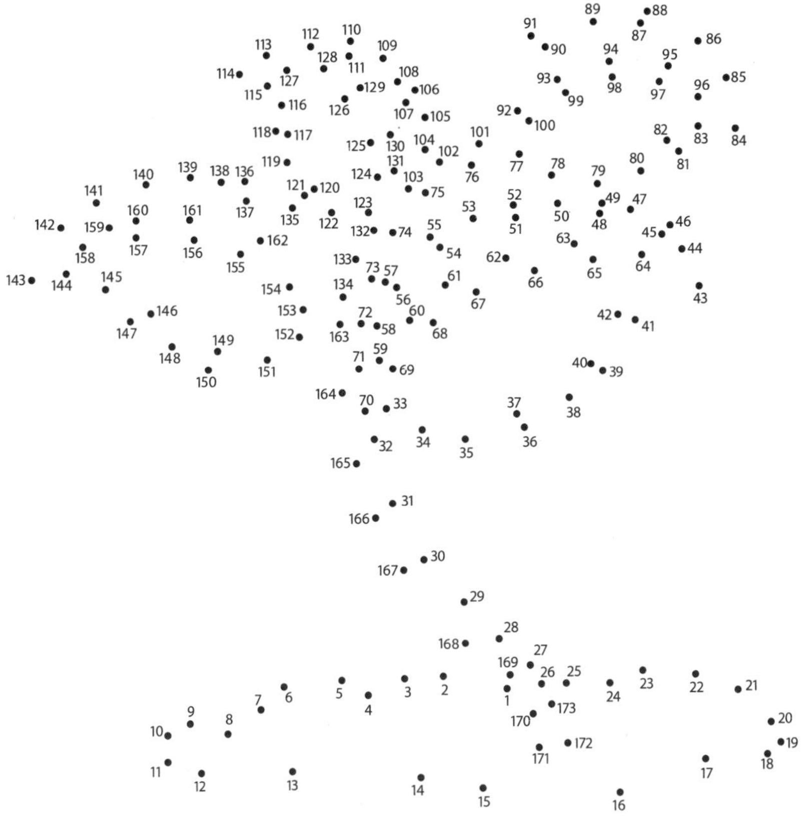

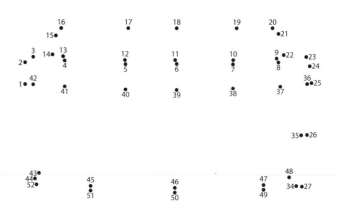

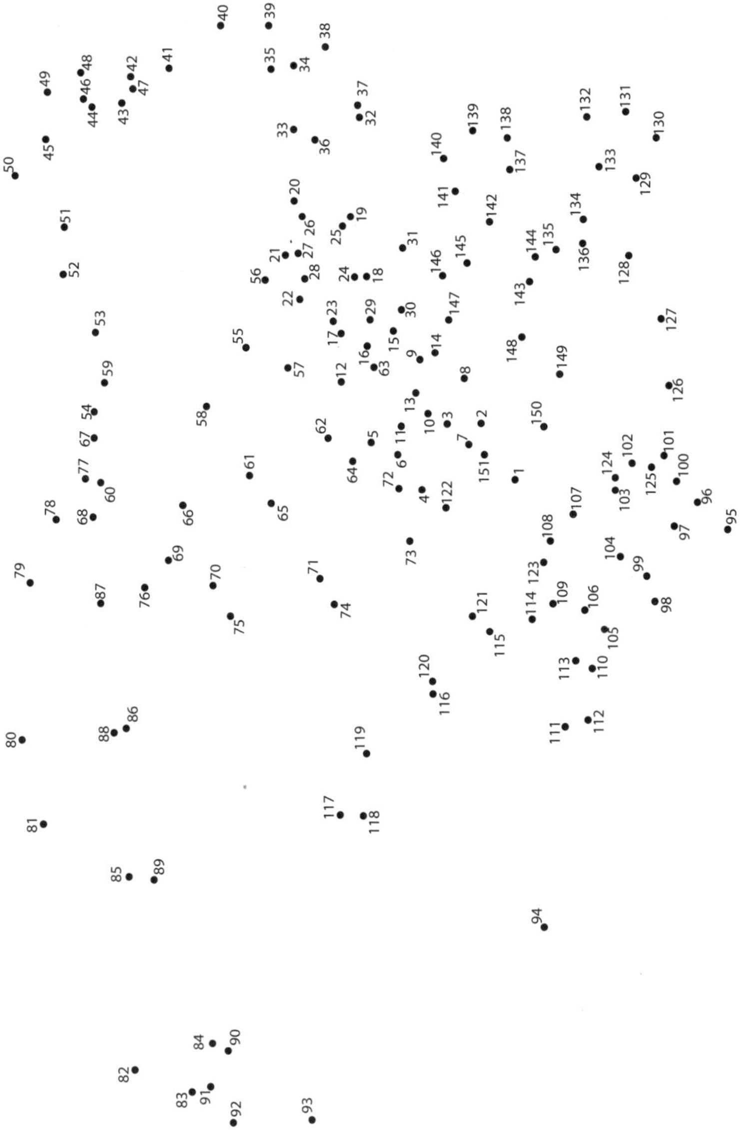

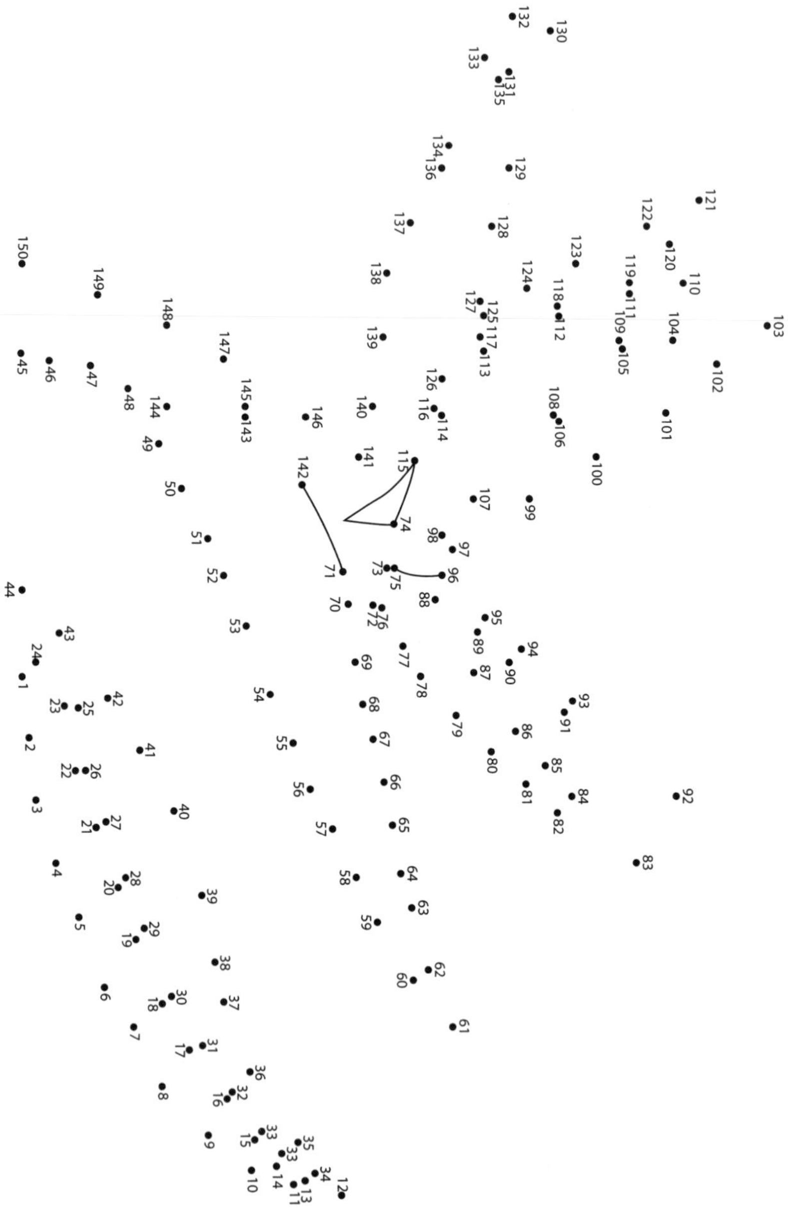

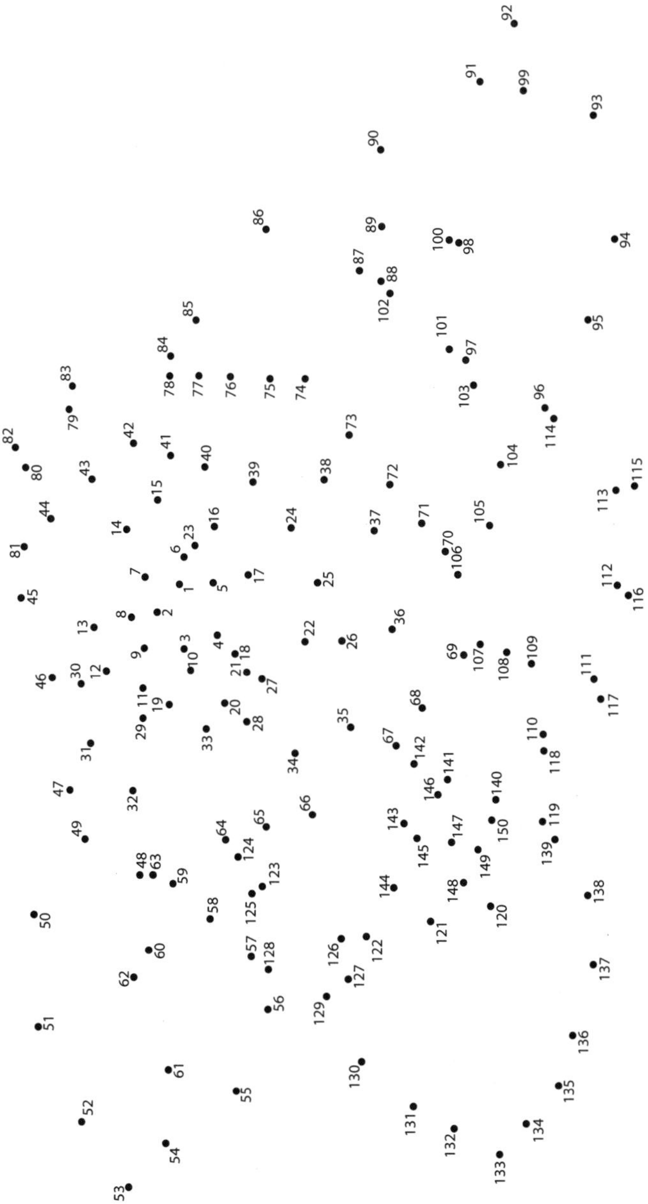

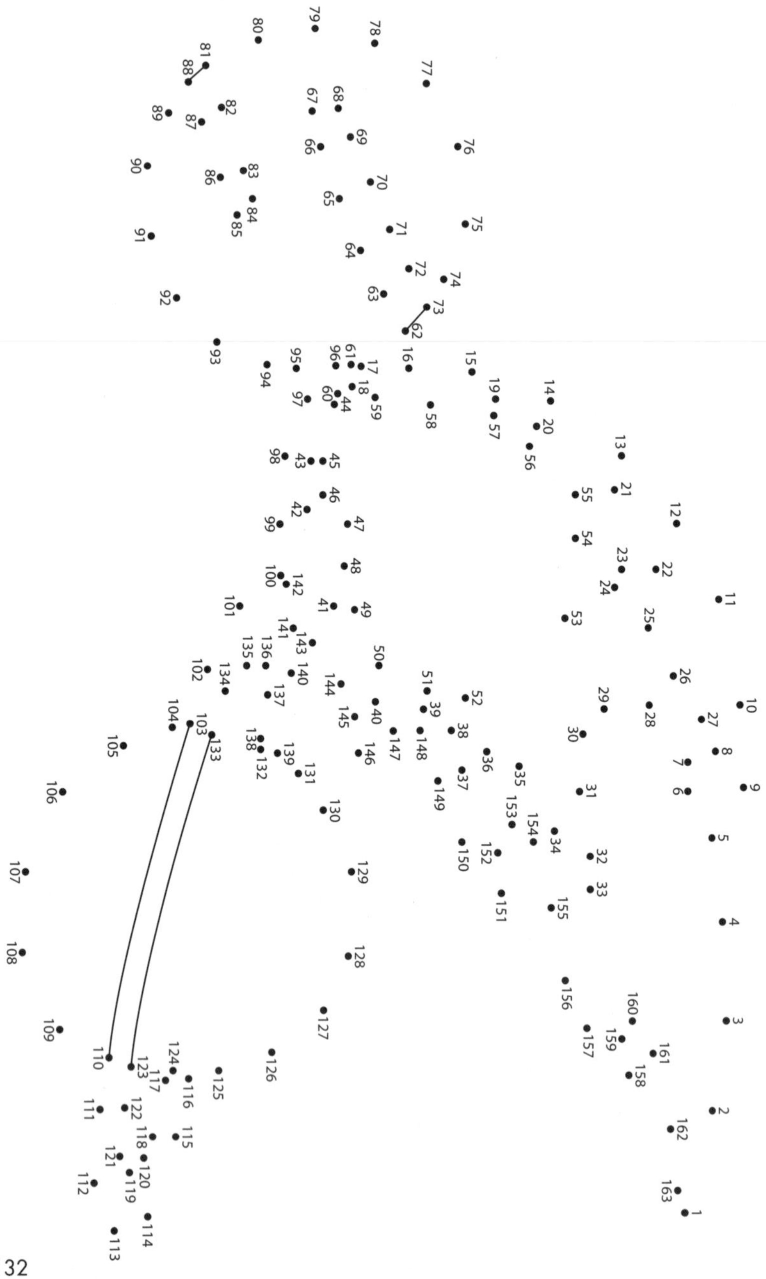

132

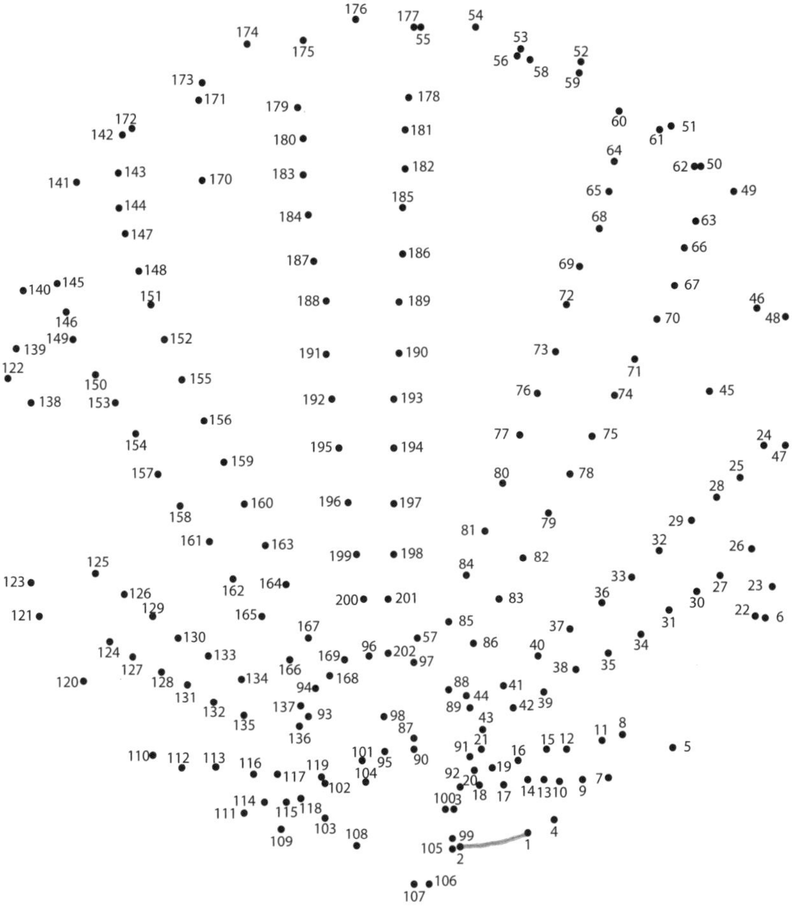

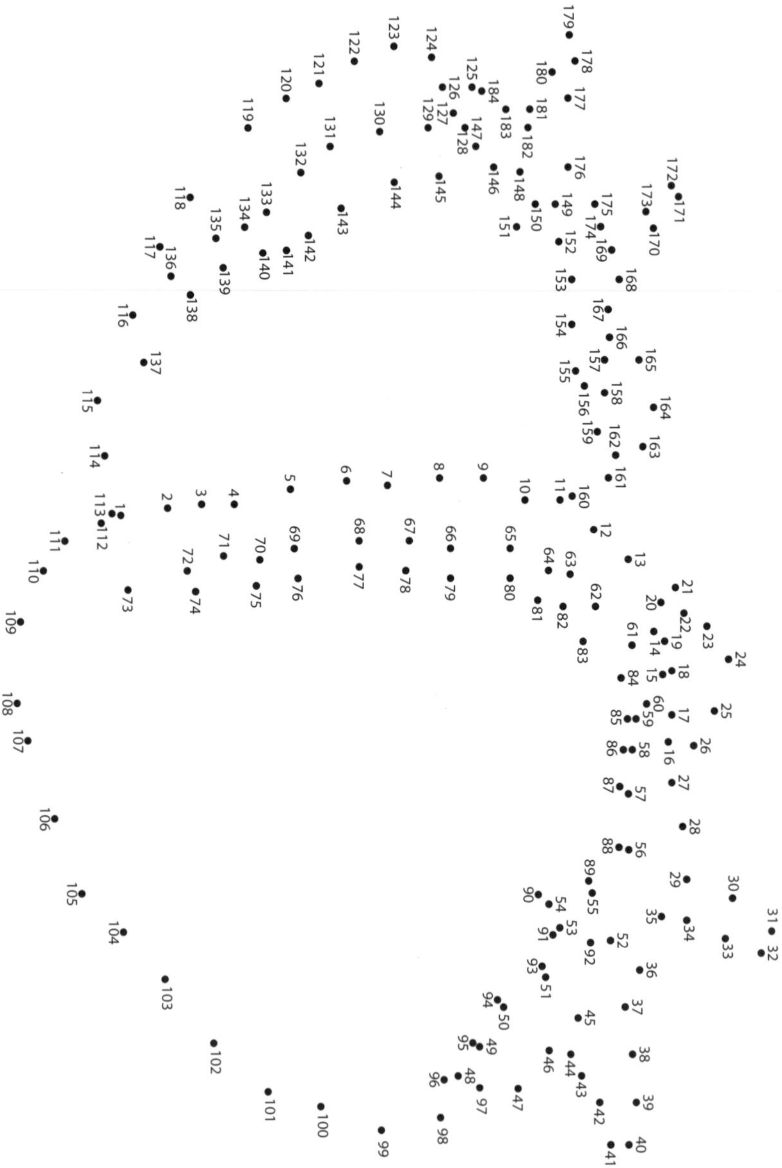

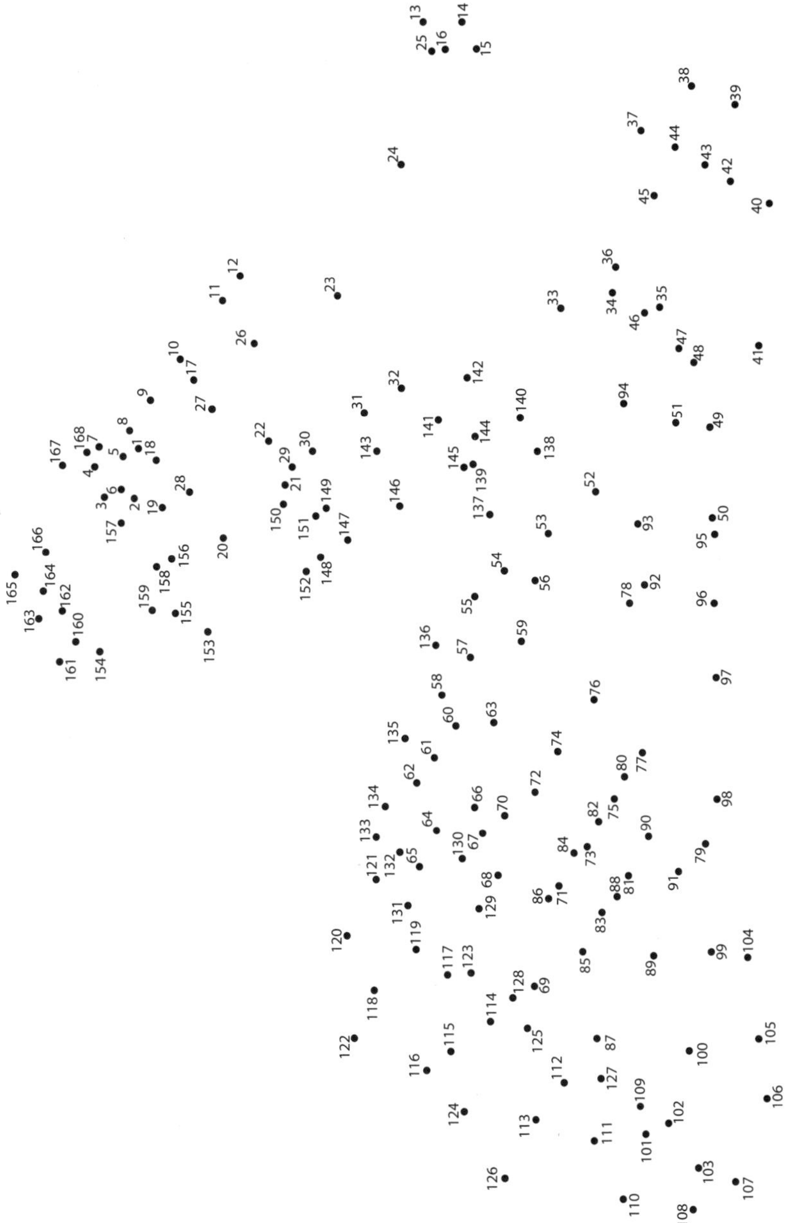

135

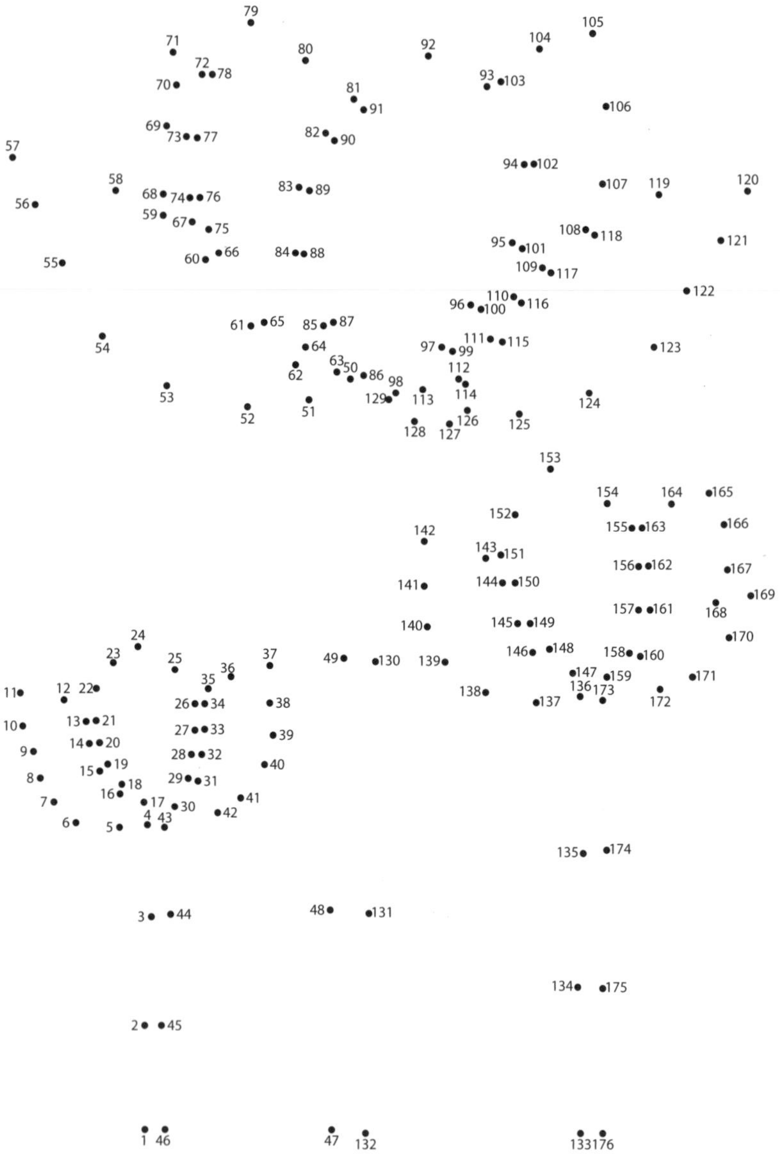

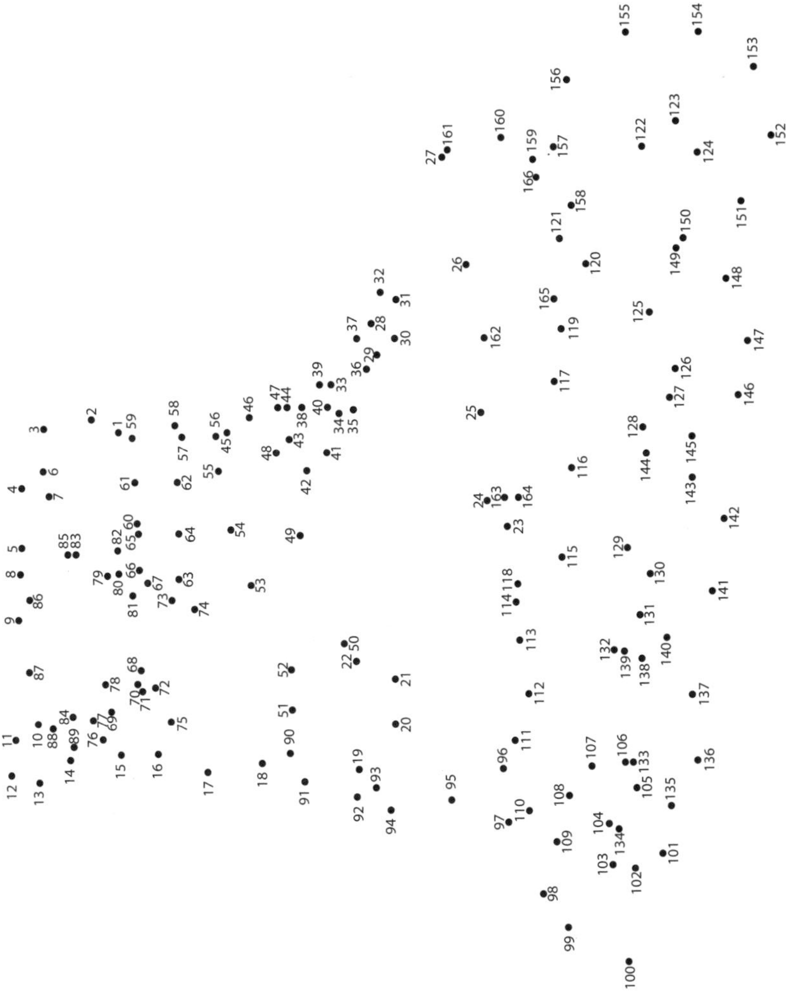

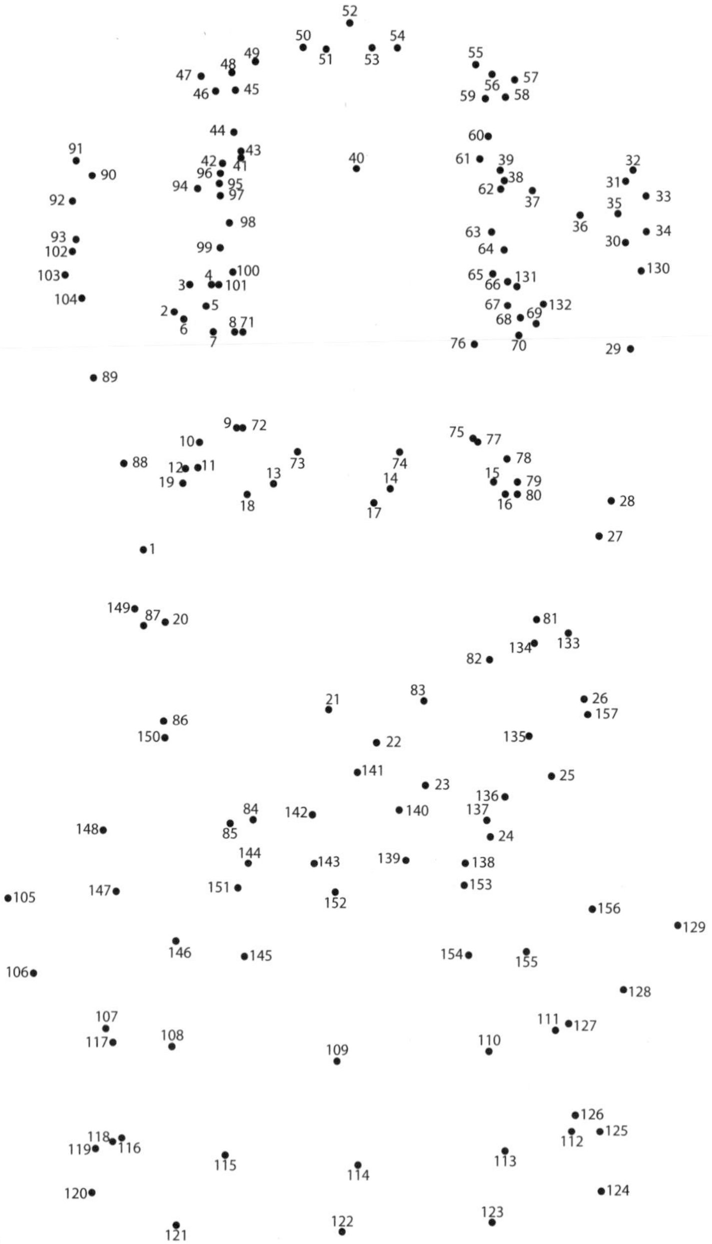

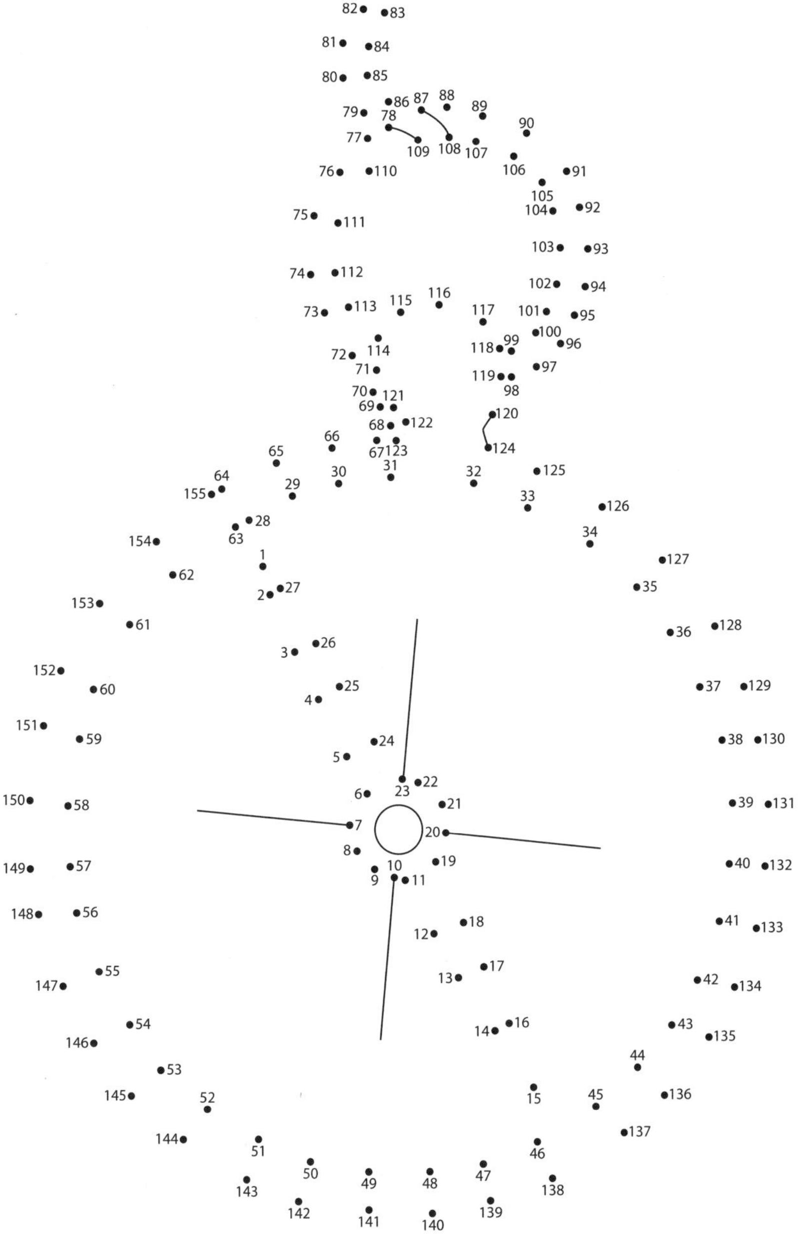

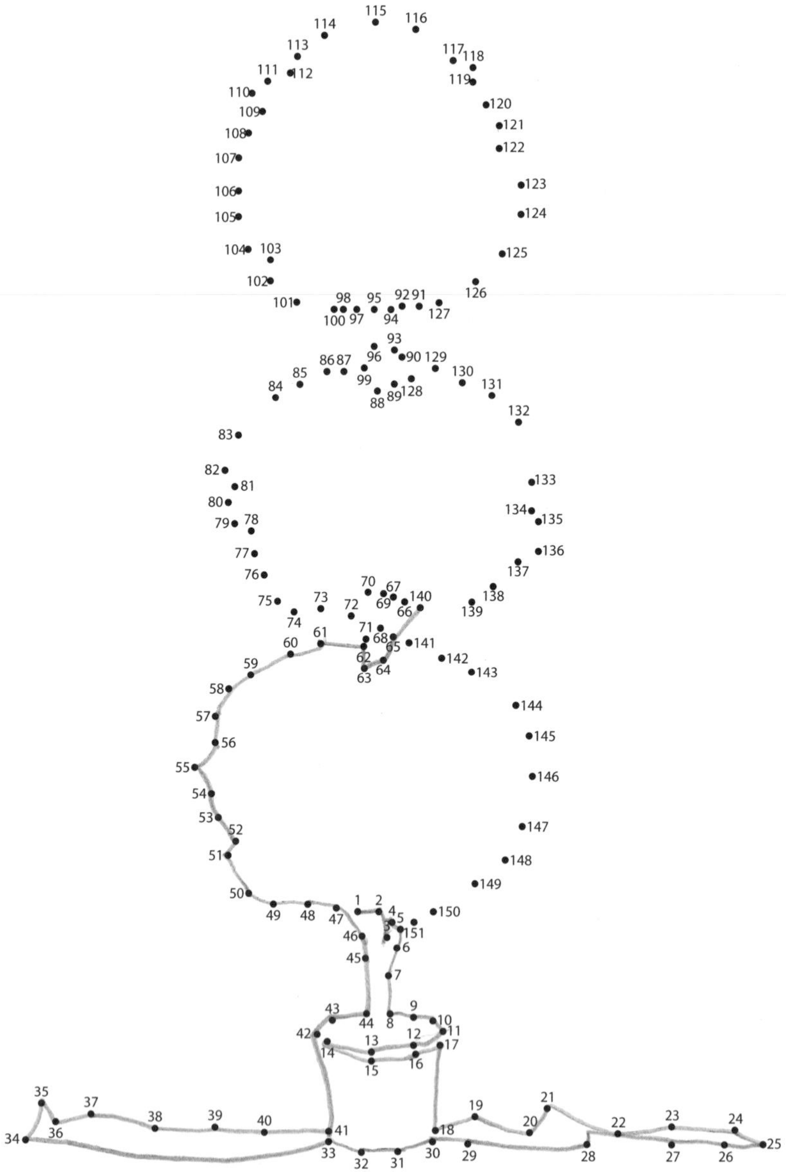

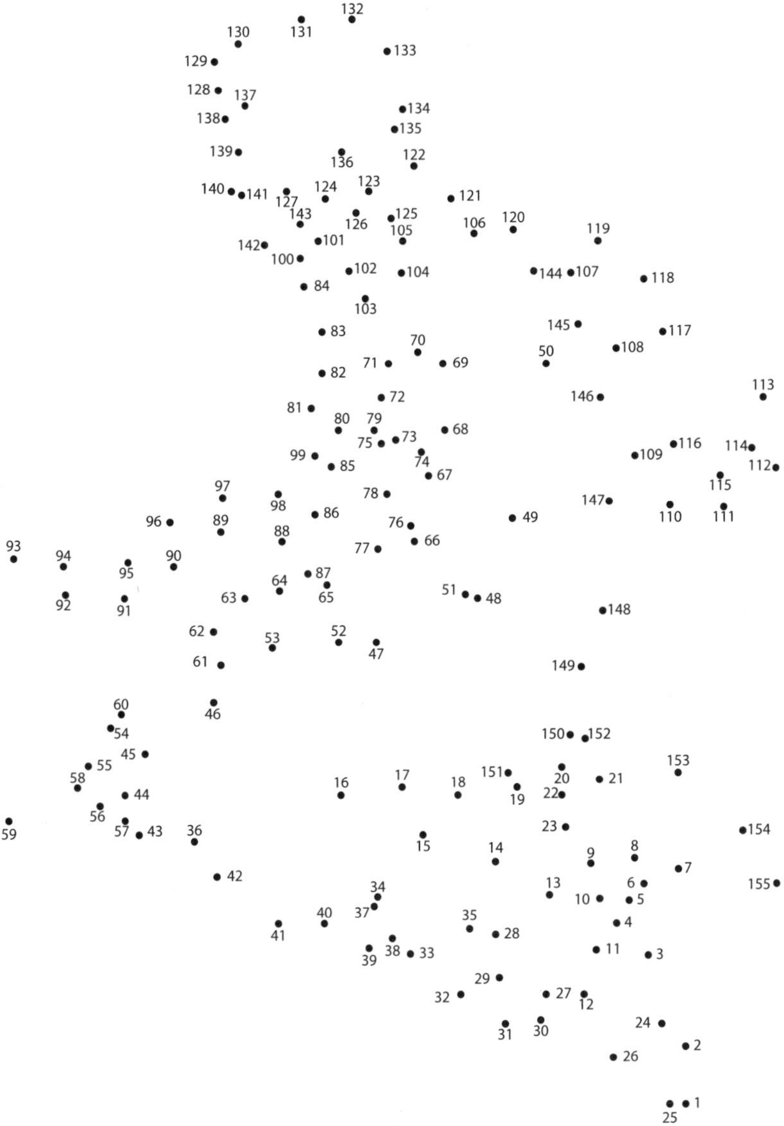

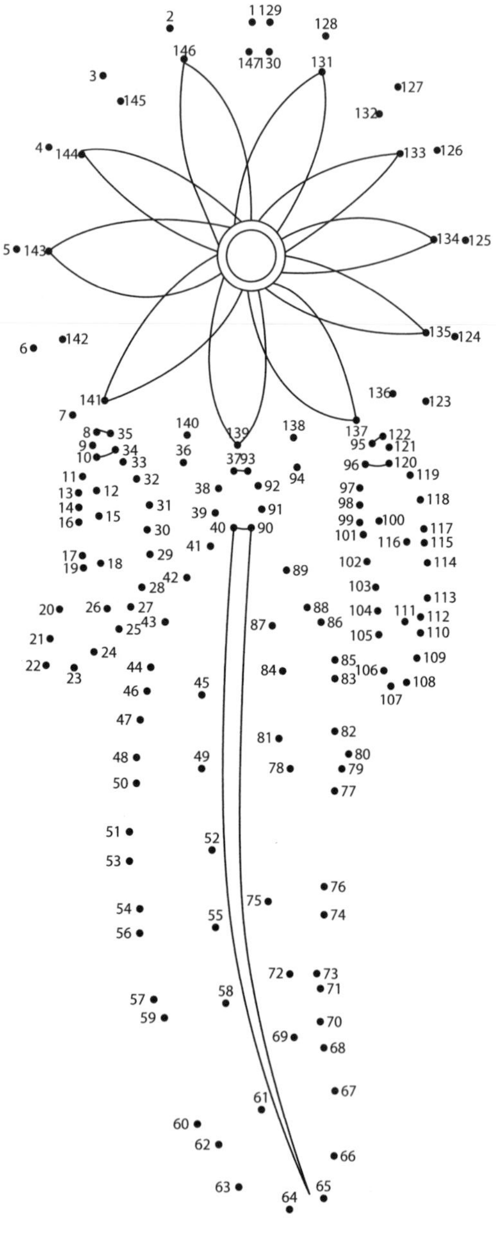
1
2
3
4
5
6
7
8
9
10
11
12
13
14
15
16
17
18
19
20
21
22
23
24
25
26
27
28
29
30
31
32
33
34
35
36
37
38
39
40
41
42
43
44
45
46
47
48
49
50
51
52
53
54
55
56
57
58
59
60
61
62
63
64
65
66
67
68
69
70
71
72
73
74
75
76
77
78
79
80
81
82
83
84
85
86
87
88
89
90
91
92
93
94
95
96
97
98
99
100
101
102
103
104
105
106
107
108
109
110
111
112
113
114
115
116
117
118
119
120
121
122
123
124
125
126
127
128
129
130
131
132
133
134
135
136
137
138
139
140
141
142
143
144
145
146
147

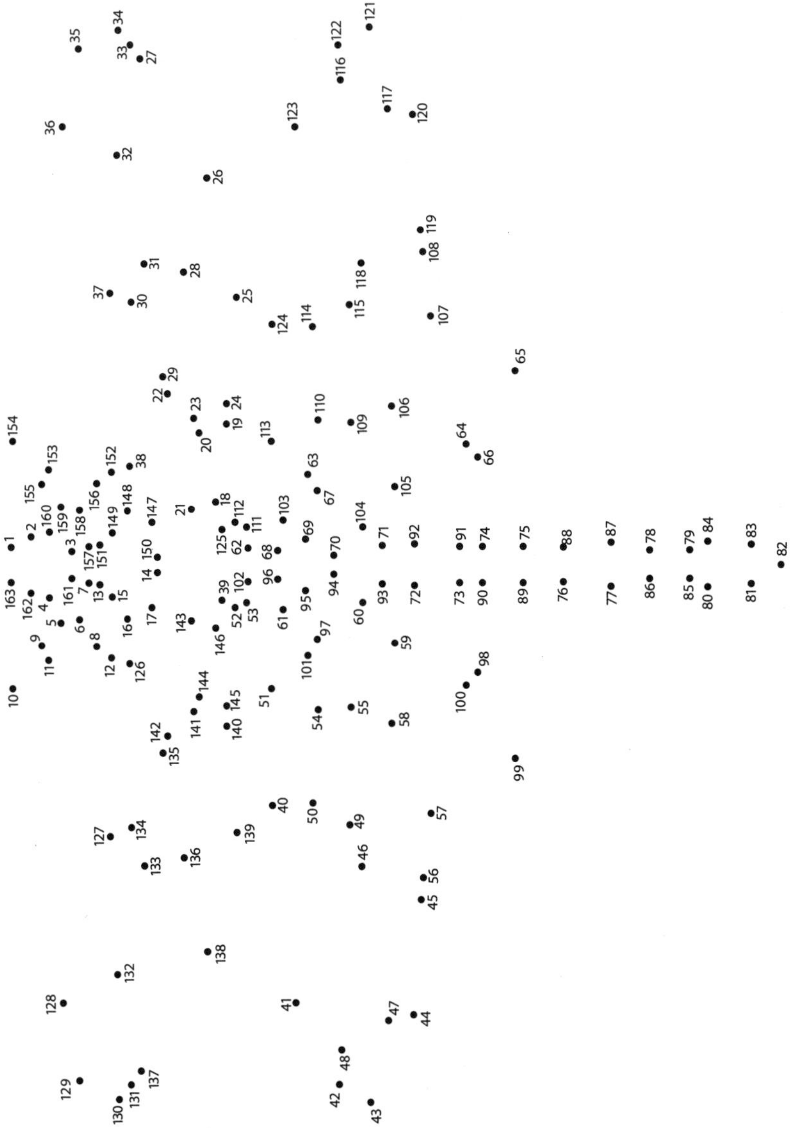

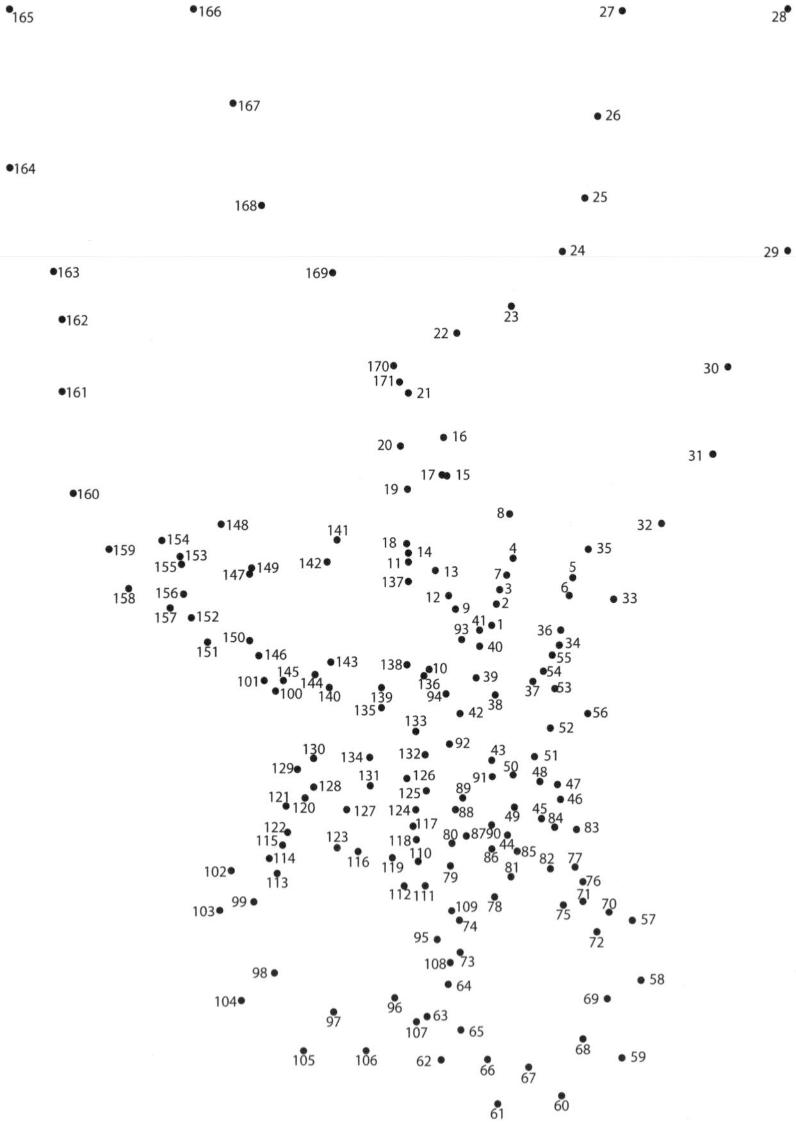

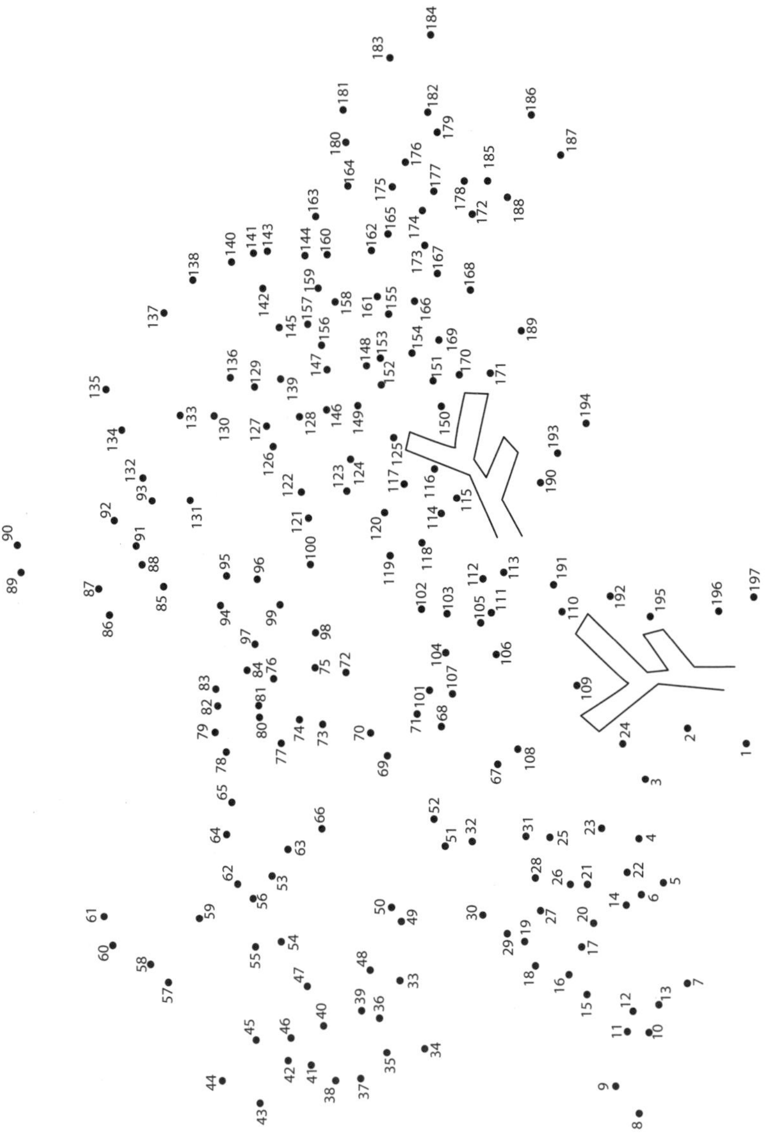

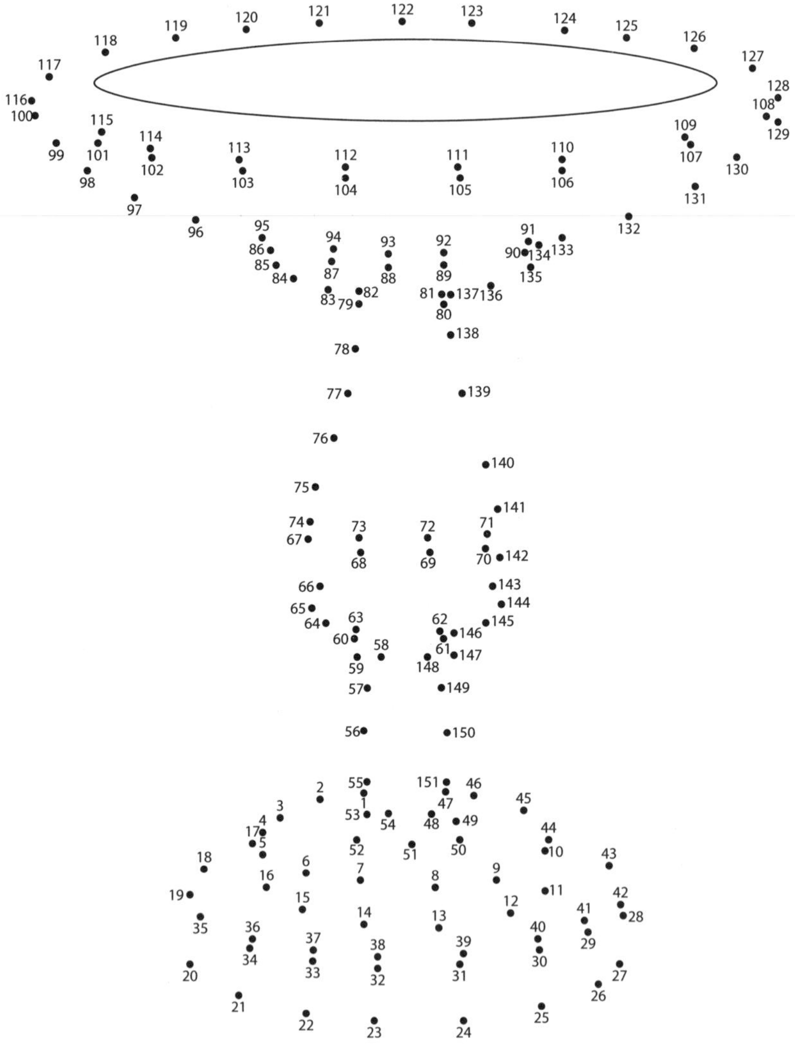

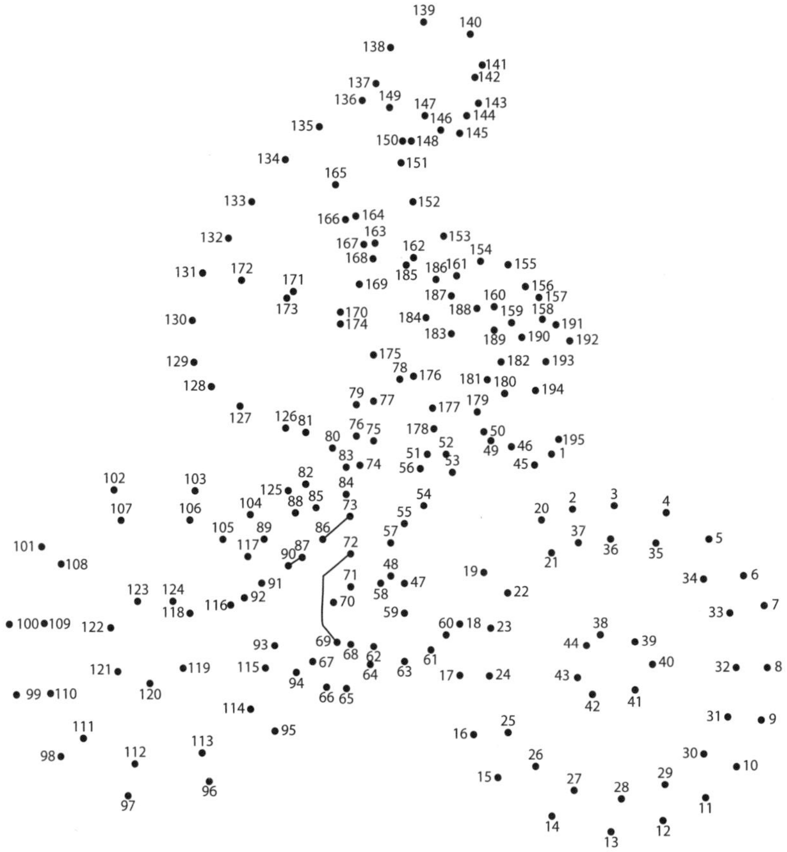

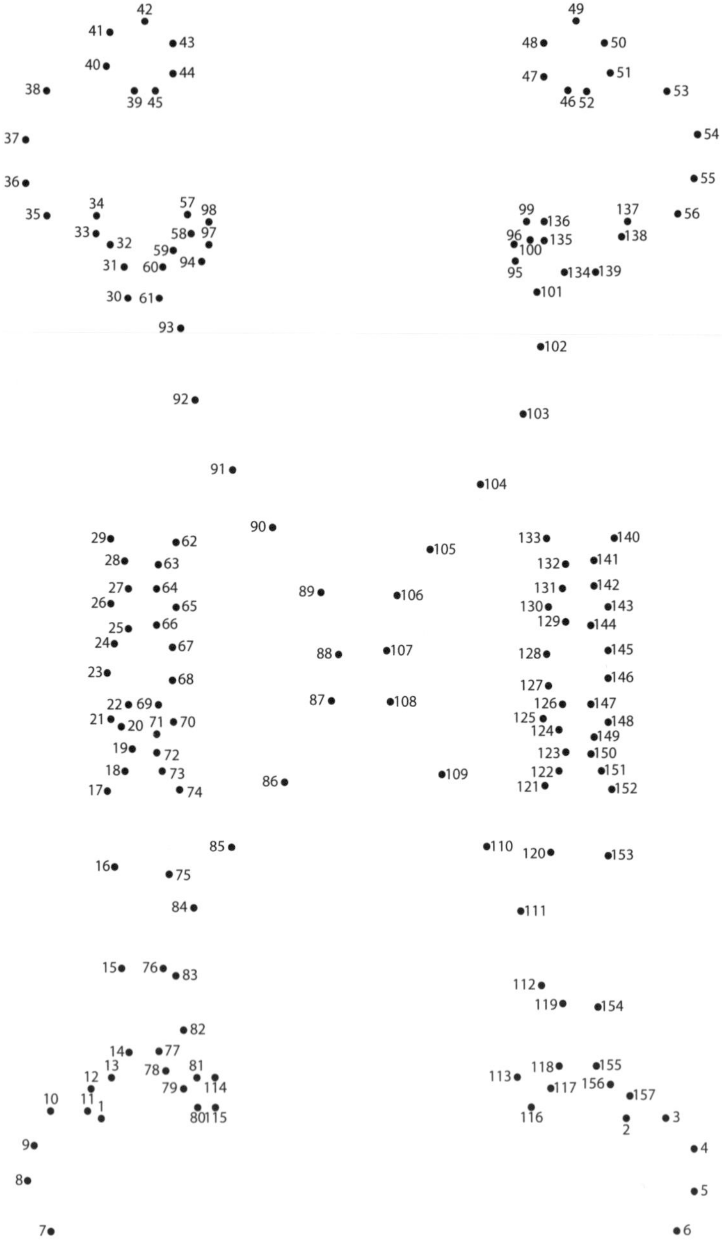

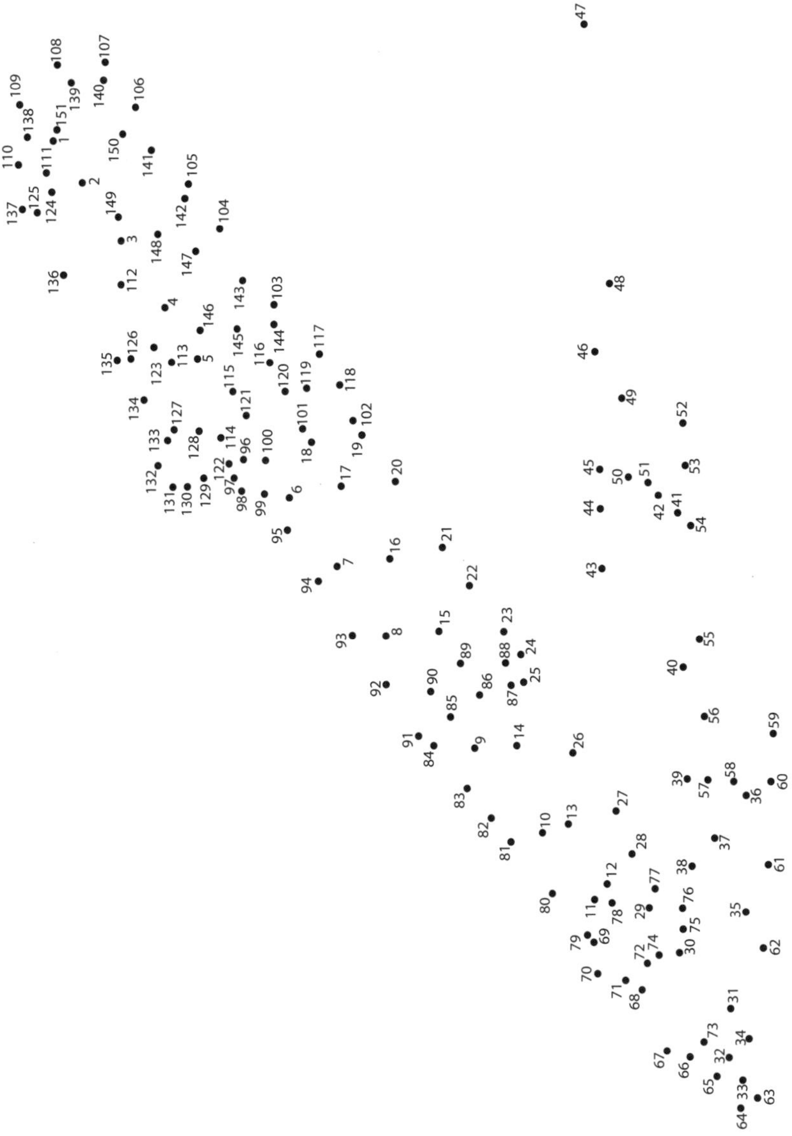

149

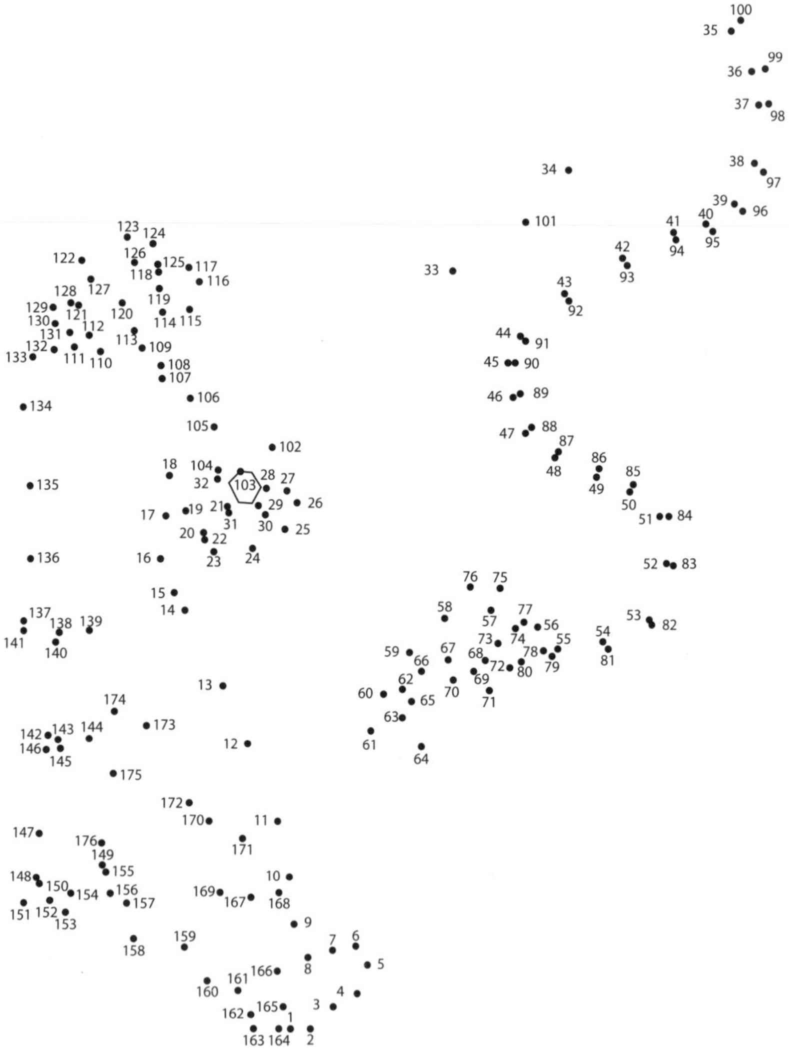

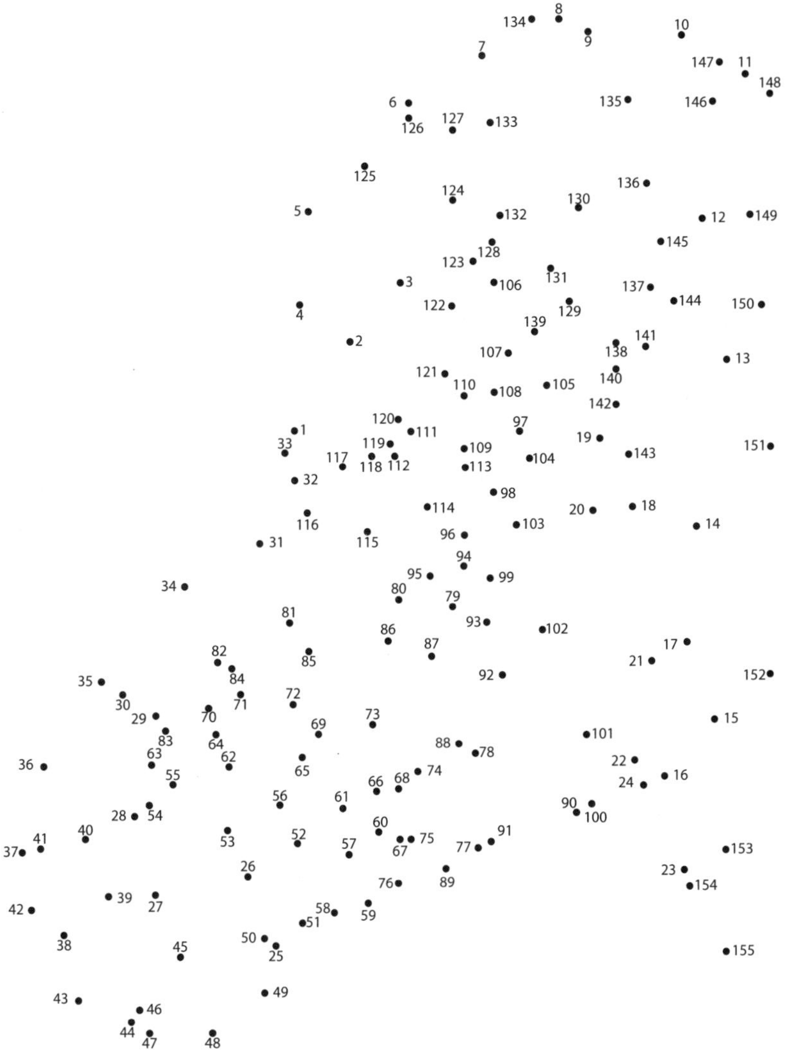

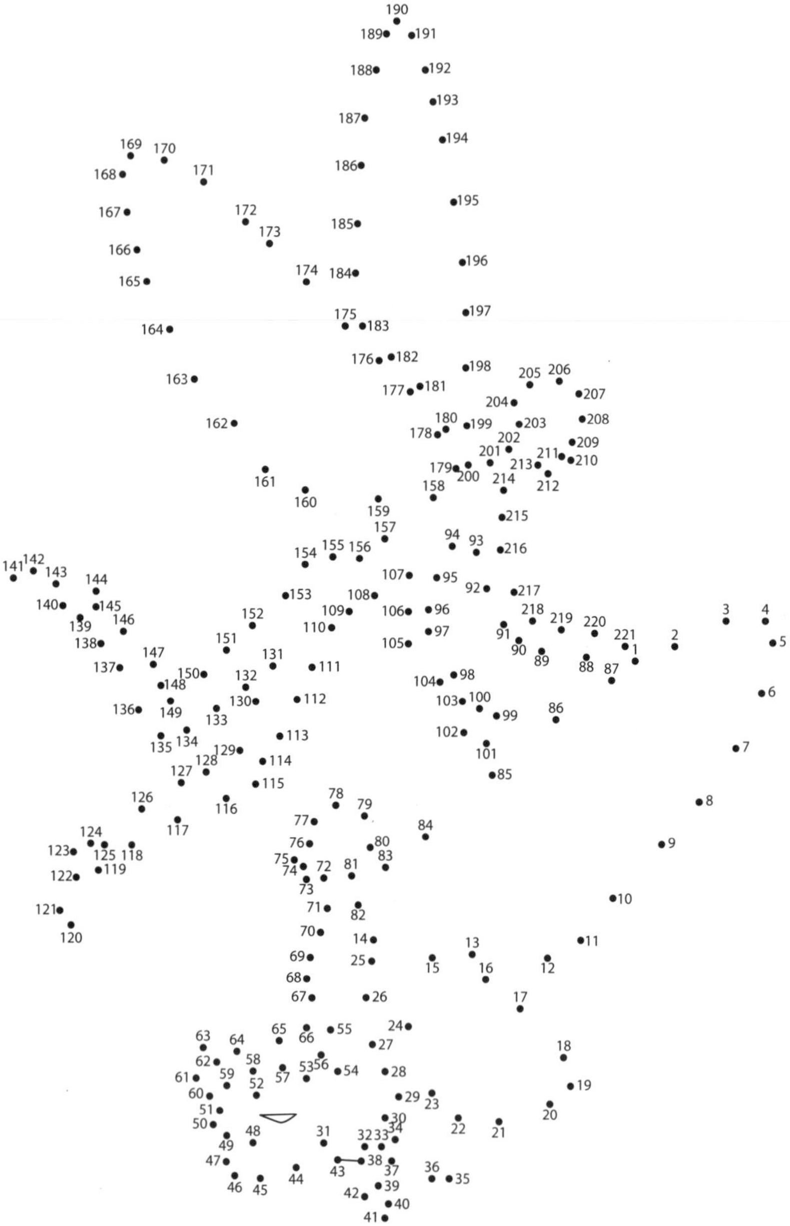

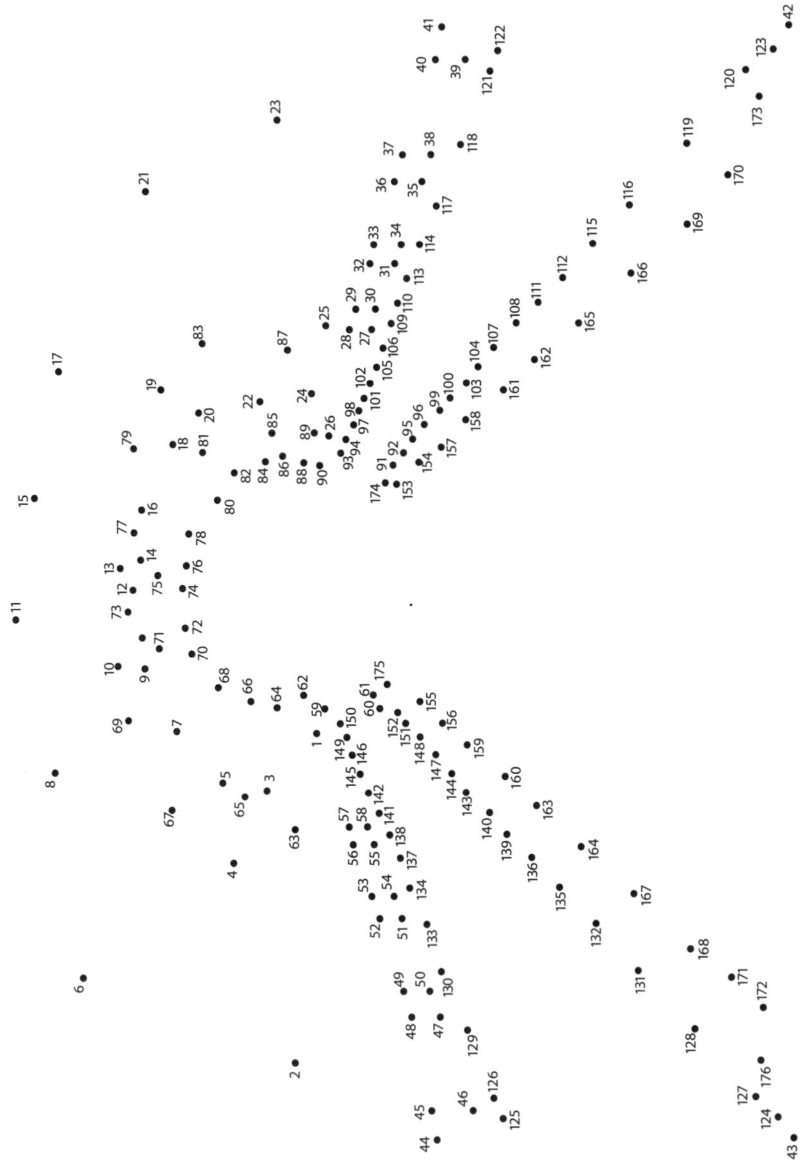

153

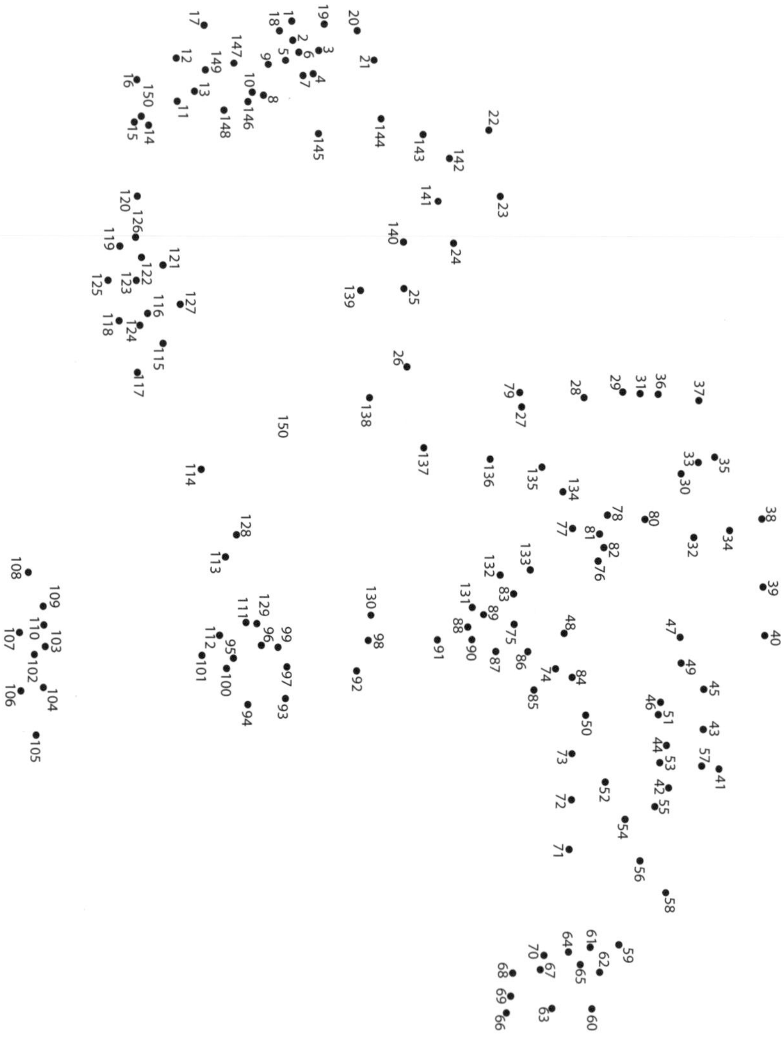

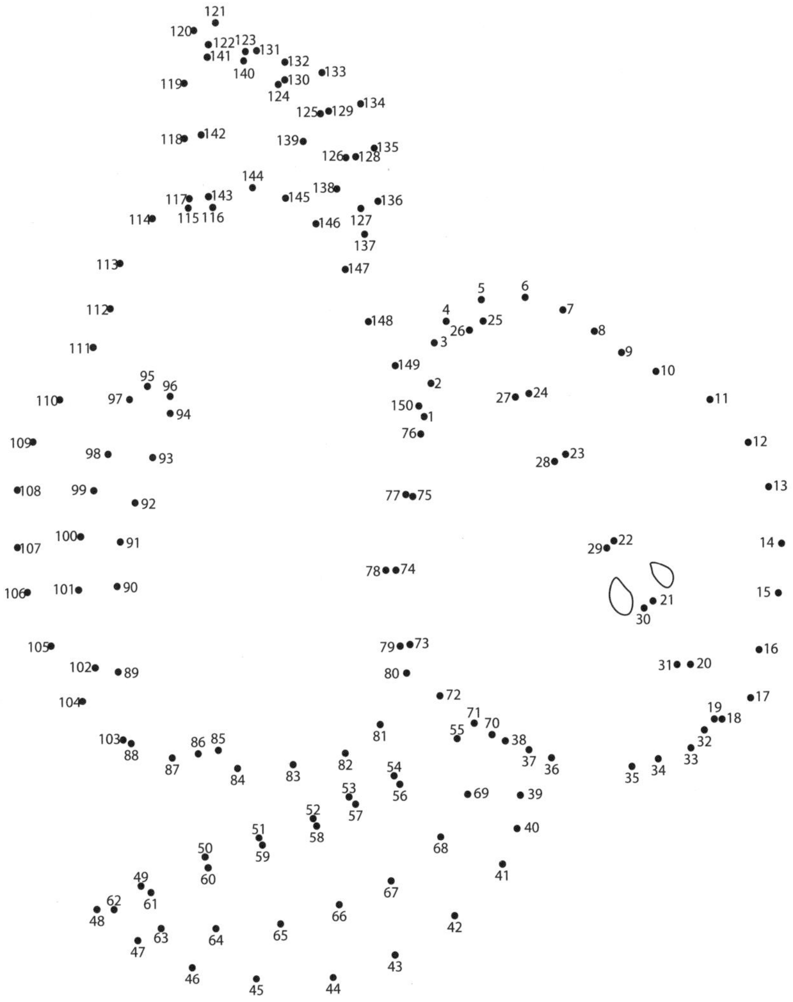

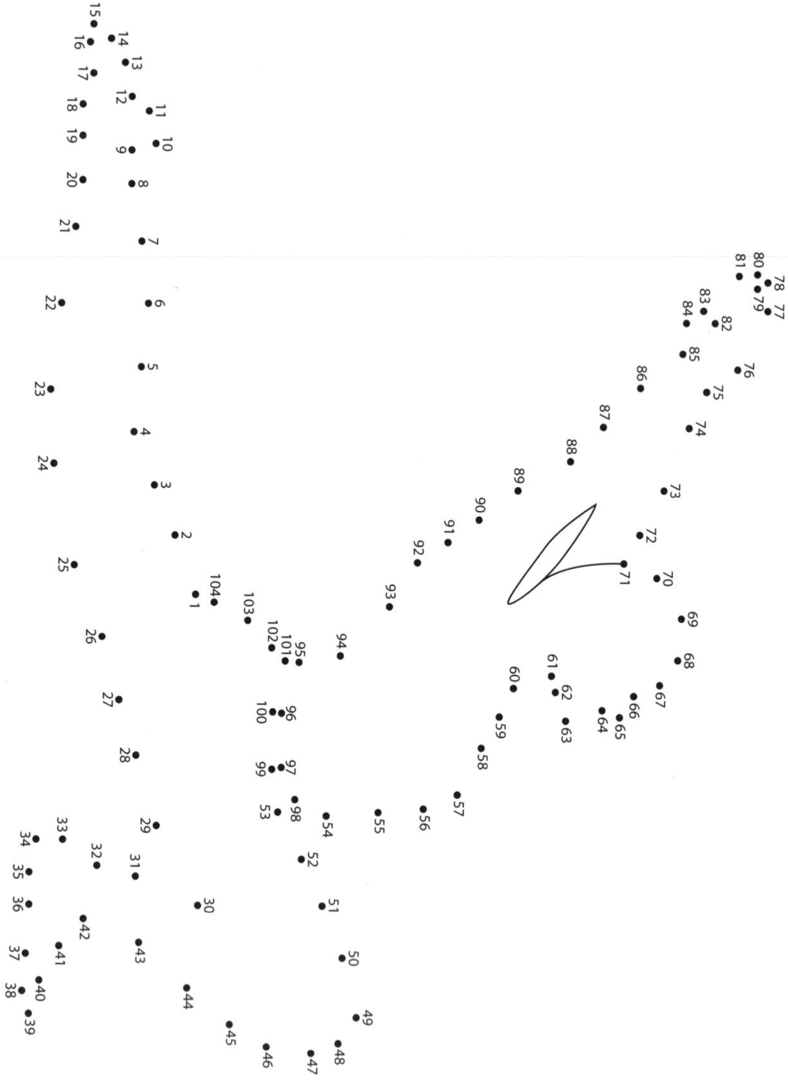

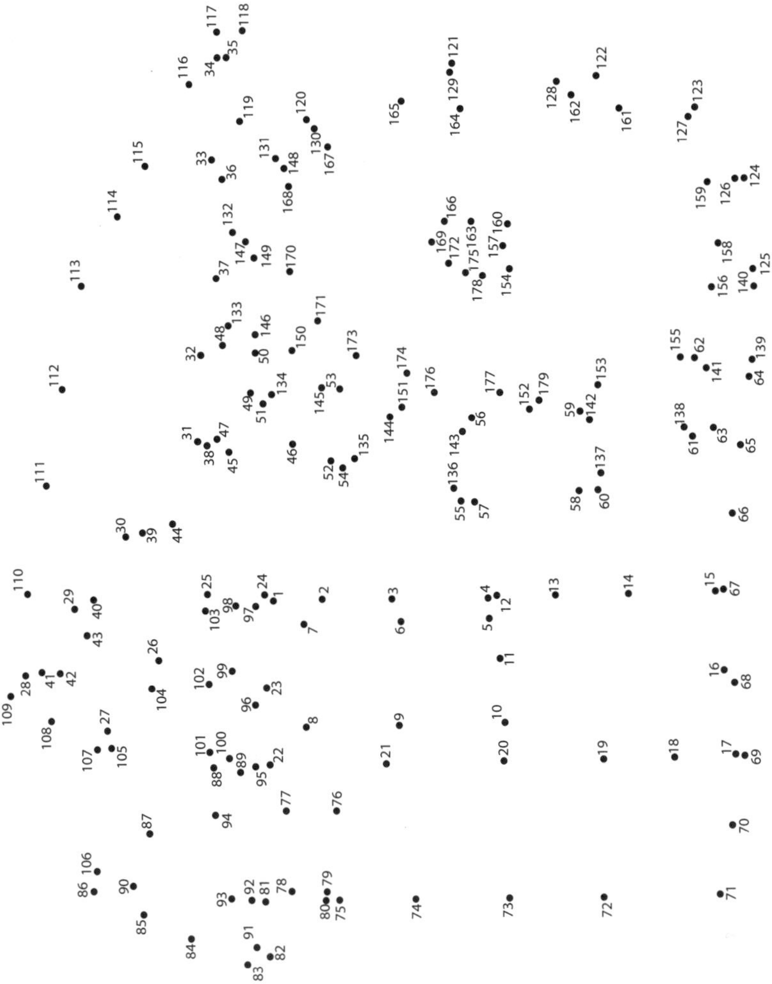

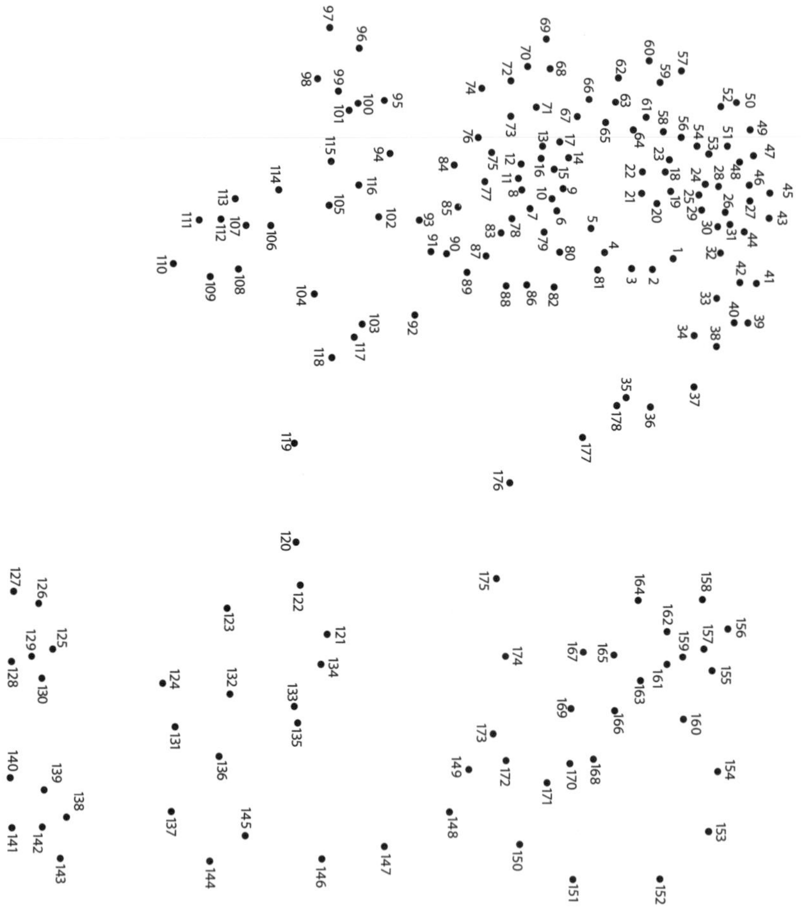

LIST OF ILLUSTRATIONS